The Elfin Knight

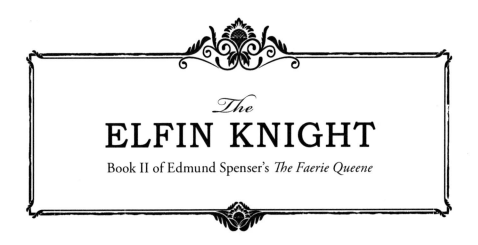

The ELFIN KNIGHT

Book II of Edmund Spenser's *The Faerie Queene*

Updated and annotated by

Toby J. Sumpter

canonpress
Moscow, Idaho

Published by Canon Press
P.O. Box 8729, Moscow, ID 83843
800–488–2034 | www.canonpress.com

Toby J. Sumpter, *The Elfin Knight: Edmund Spenser's* The Faerie Queene, *Book II.*
Copyright © 2010 by Toby J. Sumpter.

Cover design by Rachel Hoffmann and Laura Storm. Cover illustration: N. C. Wyeth,
The Boy's King Arthur (New York: Charles Scribner's Sons, 1917).
Interior design by Laura Storm.

Printed in the United States of America.

Library of Congress Cataloging-in-Publication Data

Spenser, Edmund, 1552?-1599.
  [Faerie queene. Book 2]
  The Elfin knight : Edmund Spenser's The faerie queene, book II / updated and
annotated by Toby J. Sumpter.
     p. cm.
  ISBN-13: 978-1-59128-052-1 (pbk.)
  ISBN-10: 1-59128-052-4 (pbk.)
  1. Knights and knighthood--Poetry. 2. Virtues--Poetry. 3. Spenser, Edmund,
1552?-1599. Faerie queene. Book 2. I. Sumpter, Toby J. II. Title.
  PR2358.A4S86 2010
  821'.3--dc22

                                        2010017658

10 11 12 13 14 15 16   9 8 7 6 5 4 3 2 1

For my son, River Edmond,
a true Elfin Knight.

Contents

ntroduction

Edmund Spenser is an unsung hero in Christian literature. Dante, Milton, and Shakespeare seem to get their time, but Spenser's has been a long time in coming. And with good reason, I might add, for I suspect he is far too Christian for our modern taste buds.

I first read *The Faerie Queene* in college, where I stumbled through the archaic vocabulary, arbitrary spellings, and metrical lines, and gathered a confused and rather tangled impression of the six stories in Spenser's epic. Upon learning that Spenser had intended to write twelve books, I sighed with relief. But when I began teaching medieval literature for Atlas School a couple of years later, I included Book I of *The Faerie Queene* in the form of Roy Maynard's *Fierce Wars and Faithful Loves* (Canon Press, 1999). This decision was made because it was literature that we *ought* to read, but it certainly wasn't the case that I was looking forward to it. I was teaching a group of boys ranging in age from eight to thirteen, and I warned them that the task would be difficult but rewarding (I silently hoped). However, those six weeks were some of the most rewarding weeks I have ever spent with a class. We read aloud, discussed, acted out, and drew pictures of Spenser's tale of the Redcross Knight. At the close of those weeks, it had become obvious that we had all loved the world of Faerie Land, and we were anxious to return. And thus with a bit of arranging and rearranging, I decided that we would also read Book II. It was then that I began searching for another version like Maynard's that might bridge the Elizabethan world to ours with updated spellings, definitions of archaic vocabulary, and helpful explanations along the way. When time ran short and only one out-of-print copy could be procured that *almost* fit the bill, I decided to make one myself.

It was once again a time of enchantment and adventure, and when I mention *The Faerie Queene* now, my students' faces brighten and their eyes are keen. They've regularly asked when we're going to do more and which book we'll do next. The older students have even asked to read the text in its original setting. They've been to Faerie Land, and they're willing to work even harder if it means another ride through the wilds of Spenser's imagination.

But I said that Spenser was too Christian—what of that? Spenser is too Christian in at least three glorious respects. First, Spenser is not a sentimentalist or a prude. Another way to say it is that he is not a gnostic. Moderns—Christians and non-Christians alike—have come to believe that this world is a necessary evil, but Spenser glories in the wildness and creativity of our triune God. He describes creation with exuberance and awe. He is not afraid to portray the truly gruesome nature of unchecked fury, the artificial appeals of sexual debauchery, and the physical glories of courage, beauty, and judgment.

Secondly, Spenser's world is a Faerie Land, a waterfall in which what we perceive as reality plunges into the pool of imagination. In the post-Enlightenment world, imagination and fairy tale have been looked upon with thick suspicion, particularly and most unfortunately in the Christian Church. Here, at the center of the world, where God's love has been so wildly creative, restoring a people to Himself, it is here where creativity and imagination have been so undervalued. But Spenser knew that the world God made *is* a Faerie Land and that the Scriptures are a true and lively fairy tale. And it is in this Faerie Land where true religion and theology take place, coming out of the hands and lips of courageous knights and fair maidens. In other words, because the world is supernatural and magic, it is full of meaning, brimming with symbolism. And just as the Apostle Paul looks back at the story of Abraham and sees an allegory of the Christian Church in Sarah and Isaac (Gal. 4:22–31), so too Spenser sees all of life and history teeming with symbolism, allegory, and typology. Jesus says we ought to see *Him* on every page of the Old Testament (Lk. 24:25–27), and Spenser's *Faerie Queene* is practice in growing up into the wisdom of faith. *The Faerie Queene* is a rich allegory where names are full of meaning, and the story constantly begs for readers full of faith and imagination.

Lastly, Spenser was far more Christian than we, in that he was a poet, and *The Faerie Queene* is an epic poem. Not only has modernity sought to strip us of the joy of imagination, but it has no less than relegated the world of poetry to an irrelevant aristocracy, to a dark and dusty closet on a shelf below the bowling shoes. But the world God made is far more beautiful than our dry and humorless encyclopedias. God's spoken and written word is full of poetry and drama, narrative, and rhythm. As we read Spenser, may we recover a love for well-crafted speech and lyrical poetry, and may our words and the words of our students and children grow to more fully echo His, and may there come a day when mere speech is awkward, and it's somehow more comfortable to sing.

The hero of the second book of *The Faerie Queene* is Sir Guyon, the Knight of Temperance. It has not been my desire to pick the book apart in order to explain *completely* Spenser's picture of temperance. His story is sufficient to the task. However, I have made mention here and there a few thoughts on the subject. It appears that temperance for Spenser is a correlative to holiness, the thematic virtue of Book I. The meeting of Guyon and Redcross in the first canto is hardly incidental, nor is how they meet. Their meeting means that holiness and temperance are sometimes fooled into thinking of each other as enemies, but they are truly comrades at arms.

So what is temperance? Temperance seems to be a kind of dominion and rule. It is both defensive and offensive, full of restraint and unbridled. But it is particularly concerned with the physical material of the world. Temperance is dominion over creation. Spenser spends much of the book exploring the emotions of the body like anger and lust. At other points he is concerned with those things that allure our eyes and tastes, like greed, idleness, and gluttony. In the last few cantos, Guyon learns to rule wild beasts and an evil fortress. Some literary critics have suggested that where Book I (i.e., holiness) was concerned with spiritual or supernatural enemies and struggles, Book II is aimed at the natural and material. While this may be an overly simplistic explanation, it may be a start at any rate. But the point of Redcross and Guyon's meeting at the beginning is that there is no dichotomy. The spiritual struggle is a physical struggle and vice versa. Moderns no less than the ancients still "struggle" with a right understanding of this. We too easily listen to the Archimagos of our day and charge blindly at the very virtues we need the most.

Like Redcross, Guyon is saved by Prince Arthur. Arthur is undoubtedly the Christ-figure of Spenser's tale. This serves to accentuate the fact that while "natural man" may be able to defy many of the lures of sin and the world (with the aid of Holiness and the wisdom of the Palmer), natural man no less than spiritual man is in need of a Savior and redemption. We are unable to save ourselves in either case; it is the "exceeding grace of highest God, that loves his creatures so, and all his works with mercy doth embrace" (8.1.5–7).

My intent throughout this work has merely been to make Spenser more accessible, while preserving his words, rhythm, and style. This is not a commentary on the second book of *The Faerie Queene*. And while I have updated spelling, defined archaic words, and tried to explain difficult passages, I have also refrained from explaining and defining *everything*. I do hope that many who read this still find Spenser to be challenging. I do hope it takes a bit of work. All the same, perhaps this edition will keep the adventurous reader from losing the forest due to the trees.

I have left the book's preface in its original setting so as to give the reader a glimpse of the true treasure. Throughout the rest, I have updated spellings, as I mentioned. At several points, by altering spellings, I have modified Spenser's iambic pentameter. In other instances, I've merely given the updated spelling of the word in the margin in order to preserve the original meter. Quotation marks have been added to help the reader distinguish between speeches and the like. Spenser also capitalized words far more frequently than we usually do. I have lowered the case of many. The notes are relegated to the footnotes on each page and will no doubt be too many, too few, or too muddled for many readers. Many of the notes were originally intended for my class of boys, and this certainly comes through in their form and content. Lastly, I have defined many archaic or less familiar words in the margins of each page. Hopefully I have left you a few words to look up yourself. Occasionally I have given different glosses to the same word based on the context. Those aren't typos. Likewise, I have also defined some common words throughout the beginning of the text; towards the middle and end, I've left you to the fate of your memory. But just in case you're forgetful like me, I've tried to make a pretty thorough list of those kinds of words. They are listed on the following page, so as to ease your search for their meanings.

Finally, I have included as an appendix a short play that I wrote for my students to perform. This may be helpful for other school settings. The object of the drama was to have another opportunity to reflect on Spenser's story in a different light—through incarnation. The play is not meant to be serious; in fact it's rather silly in places. I've found that the absurd is often remembered and treasured by my students; I hope you may find the same, or at the very least enjoy some time on the stage together.

Thanks to my class at Atlas School for that first ride together through Faerie Land, for the laughter, and for many serious discussions. May you boys be sons of Sir Guyon, knights of temperance all your days. And yes, I know that the cover illustration is not *really* Sir Guyon, but use your imagination— it looks pretty close doesn't it? Thanks to one of the boys' parents (I can't remember who!) who suggested I pursue having this published. Thanks also to Bill and Robin Amos for facilitating the opportunity to teach; Robin made many copies of the original drafts that first year. Thanks also to Doug Jones and the rest of the folks at Canon Press. Thanks to Elizabeth Heale, whose commentary on *The Faerie Queene* was helpful and thought provoking. She was also kind enough to respond to an email inquiry from me. My wife kindly proofread the manuscript and offered her comments and helpful suggestions. She has also lent me a good bit of time that was rightly hers. Thank you. The ball's in my court.

Toby J. Sumpter
Spruce Cottage

Commonly used words:

eke—also
eftsoones—shortly
ne—neither, nor
ere—before
nathelesse—nevertheless
withouten—without
'gan—began
ensample—example
t'(abbreviation)—to _____
sprite—person, spirit
wight—person, creature, living thing
mote—might, may
puissance—strength, might
hight—called, named

THE SECOND BOOKE OF THE FAERIE QVEENE.
Contayning
THE LEGEND OF SIR GVYON.
OR
OF TEMPERAVNCE.[1]

Right well I wote° most mighty Soueraine,	*know*
That all this famous antique history,	
Of some th'aboundance of an idle braine	
Will iudged° be, and painted forgery,	*judged*
Rather then matter of iust° memory,	*just*
Sith° none, that breatheth liuing° aire, does know,	*since / living*
Where is that happy land of Faerie,	
Which I so much do vaunt°, yet no where show,	*praise*
But vouch antiquities, which no body can know.[2]	

But let that man with better sence aduize°,	*advise*
That of the world least part to vs is red°:	*read*
And dayly how through hardy enterprize,	
Many great Regions are discouered,	
Which to late age were neuer mentioned.	
Who euer heard of th'Indian *Peru?*	
Or who in venturous vessell measured	
The *Amazon* huge riuer now found trew?	
Or fruitfullest *Virginia* who did euer vew?[3]	

---

1. This is Edmund Spenser's original preface to the second book of *The Faerie Queene.* No spellings have been changed so the reader can see with his own eyes the way the author originally wrote his tale. Watch carefully—Spenser uses the letter "i" instead of "j" and the letter "u" instead of "v" (among other things!).

2. Spenser addresses his writing to his "Sovereign," meaning his Queen, Elizabeth I. He says that he knows some people will judge his story to be merely made up, a "painted forgery." This is the case, he says, because no one knows where Faerie Land is.

3. Spenser says that wise men will know that many lands are constantly being discovered like Peru or the Amazon or Virginia. These new lands are proof that Faerie Land may be found if searched for.

Yet all these were, when no man did them know;
Yet haue from wisest ages hidden beene:
And later times things more vnknowne shall show.
Why then should witlesse man so much misweene°   *misjudge / be mistaken*
That nothing is, but that which he hath seene?
What if within the Moones faire shining spheare?
What if in euery other starre vnseene
Of other worldes he happily should heare?
He wōder° would much more: yet such to some appeare.   *wonder*

Of Faerie lond yet if he more inquire,
By certaine signes here set in sundry place
He may it find; ne° let him then admire,   *nor*
But yield his sence to be too blunt and bace,
That no'te° without an hound fine footing trace.   *could not*
And thou, O fairest Princess under sky,
In this fair mirrhour maist behold thy face,
And thine owne realmes in lond of Faery,
And in this antique Image thy great auncestry.[4]

The which O pardon me thus to enfold
In couert vele, and wrap in shadowes light,
That feeble eyes your glory may behold,
Which else could not endure those beames bright,
But would be dazled with exceeding light.
O pardon, and vouchsafe with patient eare
The braue aduentures of this Faery knight
The good Sir *Guyon* gratiously to heare,
In whom great rule of Temp'raunce goodly doth appeare.[5]

4. Here Spenser gives a brief description of the whole story to follow. He aims to tell a
story that is a mirror of the English Queen, her history, and the land of England.

5. Spenser begs the pardon of his Queen because he will tell of her under a "covert
veil," that is, he will tell a story over top of her story. He says he will do this because otherwise feeble eyes would not be able to behold her "exceeding light." The overlaid story,
he says, will be the adventures of a Faerie knight, the good Sir Guyon who will show forth
the virtue of temperance. And thus the story begins.

Canto I.

Guyon by Archimago abused,
The Redcross knight awaits,
Finds Mordant and Amavia slain
With pleasure's poisoned baits.

1

That cunning architect of cankered guile,
Whom Prince's late displeasure left in bands,[1]
For falséd letters and suborned wile°,   *plot*
Soon as the Redcross knight he understands,
To been departed out of Eden lands,
To serve again his sovereign Elfin Queen,
His arts he moves, and out of caitiffs'° hands   *capturers'*
Himself he frees by secret means unseen;
His shackles empty left, himself escapéd clean.

2

And forth he fares full of malicious mind,
To worken° mischief and avenging woe,   *work*
Where ever he that godly knight may find,
His only heart-sore, and his only foe,
Since Una now he algates° must forgo,   *always*
Whom his victorious hands did earst° restore   *recently*

1. For those of you who have read Book I, this is our old friend, the devious magician Archimago, at it again!

To native crown and kingdom lately go:
Where she enjoys sure peace for evermore,
As weather-beaten ship arrived on happy shore.

3

Him therefore now the object of his spite
And deadly food he makes: him to offend
By forged treason, or by open fight
He seeks, of all his drift the aimed end:
Thereto his subtle engines he does bend
His practic° wit, and his fair filed tongue,   *experienced*
With thousand other sleights: for well he kenned°,   *knew*
His credit now in doubtful balance hung;
For hardly could be hurt, who was already stung.[2]

4

Still as he went, he crafty stales° did lay   *baits*
With cunning trains° him to entrap un'wares.   *traps*
And privy spials° placed in all his way,   *secret agents*
To weet° what course he takes, and how he fares;   *find out*
To catch him at a vantage° in his snares.   *weakness*
But now so wise and wary° was the knight   *careful*
By trial of his former harms and cares,
That he descried°, and shunnéd° still his sleight°:   *endured / guarded / wit*
The fish that once was caught, new bait will hardly bite.

5

Nathlesse° the enchanter would not spare his pain,   *nevertheless*
In hope to win occasion to his will;
Which when he long awaited had in vain,
He changed his mind from one to other ill:
For to all good he enemy was still.[3]
Upon the way him fortunéd to meet,
Fair marching underneath a shady hill,
A goodly knight, all armed in harness meet,
That from his head no place appearéd to his feet.

2. When you know where the bees' nest is, you tend to stay away. Archimago knows it will be more difficult to assault Redcross this time since Redcross will be on his guard.

3. Archimago waited for a while in order to trap Redcross. But when no opportunity presented itself, he took what he could get.

6

His carriage was full comely and upright,
His countenance demure and temperate,
But yet so stern and terrible in sight,
That cheered his friends, and did his foes amate°:   *dismay*
He was an Elfin born of noble state,
And mickle° worship in his native land;   *great*
Well could he tourney and in lists debate°,   *fight in tournaments*
And knighthood took of good Sir Huon's hand,
When with king Oberon he came to Faerie Land.[4]

7

Him als° accompanied upon the way   *also*
A comely Palmer, clad in black attire,
Of ripest years, and hairs all hoary gray,
That with a staff his feeble steps did stire°,   *guide*
Lest his long way his agéd limbs should tire:
And if by looks one may the mind aread,
He seemed to be a sage and sober sire,
And ever with slow pace the knight did lead,
Who taught his trampling steed with equal steps to tread.[5]

8

Such when as Archimago them did view,
He weened° well to work some uncouth wile,   *thought*
Eftsoones° untwisting his deceitful clew°,   *soon / plot*
He 'gan° to weave a web of wicked guile,   *began*
And with fair countenance and flattering style,
To them approaching, thus the knight bespake:
"Fair son of Mars, that seek with warlike spoil.
And great achievements great yourself to make,
Vouchsafe° to stay your steed for humble miser's sake."[6]   *decide*

9

He stayed his steed for humble miser's sake,
And bad° tell on the tenor° of his plaint°;   *asked him / nature / trouble*

4. This is Sir Guyon our hero, our champion, our Knight of Temperance. He's not all
those things at once mind you, but he's well on his way.

5. Sir Guyon is traveling on a horse, and beside him walks an old Palmer, a man of
many years who is Guyon's trusty guide.

6. Archimago has assumed the beggar's cloth hoping to secure some pity.

Who feigning° then in every limb to quake,   *pretending*
Through inward fear, and seeming pale and faint
With piteous moan his piercing speech 'gan° paint;[7]   *began*
"Dear Lady how shall I declare thy case,
Whom late I left in languorous° constraint?   *weak*

7. Archimago's putting on a show as if he's really scared.

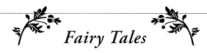

Fairy Tales

Fairy tales are an important part of healthy Christian living. They are not simply "made up" stories with no impact or relation to real life or how we actually live. In fact, the history of the world is a beautifully told fairy tale. The story begins in a perfect garden with a man, a woman, a forbidden fruit, and a crafty dragon. There in the opening chapter of God's story, He reveals the theme of History: the struggle between the seed of the woman and the offspring of the dragon. The story unravels its tapestry of tales through centuries casting this same battle again and again showing the faithful woman and her children doing battle with the dragon and his crafty sons. The struggle climaxes at the Cross where Jesus defeats the dragon through his death and resurrection. We, who are God's people, are united to Christ and share in His victory.

This Gospel and all of history show emphatically that we do not live in a sterile, naturalistic universe. The world that the triune God created is filled with tales of giants and wizards, prophets and floods, fair ladies and dragons, angels and rainbows, magic and miracles. We live in a world where water comes out of the sky, fire shoots out of mountains, and millions of stars whirl above our heads. The God who made this world is a brilliant and excessively imaginative God. At least one way in which we honor and image our Creator is through recreating and imitating His arts. The stories we tell and paint and live ought to be filled with the same sorts of mind blowing events and details. The secularists and evolutionists are boring and uninteresting with their chance and arid naturalism. But we are the sons and daughters of a God who plays with dragons, dances over His people, and became a man for our salvation. We live in a faerie land, and we can't help but love fairy tales because we are in the middle of one.

Would God thyself now present were in place,
To tell this rueful° tale; thy sight could win thee grace.⁸   *awful*

10

"Or rather would, O would it so had chanced,
That you, most noble sir, had present been,
When that lewd° ribald° with vile lust advanced   *immoral / wicked person*
Laid first his filthy hands on virgin clean,
To spoil her dainty corpse so fair and sheen,
As on the earth, great mother of us all,
With living eye more fair was never seen,
Of chastity and honor virginal:
Witness ye heavens, whom she in vain to help did call."⁹

11

"How may it be," said then the knight half wroth°,   *angered*
"That knight should knighthood ever so have shent°?"   *shed*
"None but that saw," quoth° he, "would ween° for troth°,   *said / know / certain*
How shamefully that maid he did torment.
Her looser golden locks he rudely rent,
And drew her on the ground, and his sharp sword,
Against her snowy breast he fiercely bent,
And threatened death with many a bloody word;
Tongue hates to tell the rest, that eye to see abhorred."

12

Therewith amovéd from his sober mood,
"And lives he yet," said he, "that wrought this act,
And doen° the heavens afford him vital food?"   *do*
"He lives," quoth° he "and boasteth of the fact,   *said*
Nor yet hath any knight his courage cracked."
"Where may that treachor° then," said he, "be found,   *traitor*
Or by what means may I his footing tract°?"   *track*
"That shall I show," said he, "as sure, as hound
The stricken deer doth challenge by the bleeding wound."¹⁰

8. Archimago, laying it on thick, says, "If only you were telling this story; it would win you much favor."
9. Archimago has told Guyon that some villain has just dishonored a young maiden. He calls the heavens to witness, perhaps alluding to Deuteronomy 22:27, where a betrothed maiden was not held liable for rape if it occurred in the countryside because she "cried out, but there was no one to save her."
10. Guyon asks if the villain is still alive, Archimago says he is, Guyon asks where he is, and Archimago says he'll take him to him.

13

He stayed not longer talk, but with fierce ire°   *wrath*
And zealous haste away is quickly gone
To seek that knight, where him that crafty squire[11]
Supposed to be. They do arrive anon°,   *soon*
Where sat a gentle lady all alone,
With garments rent, and hair disheveled,
Wringing her hands, and making piteous moan;
Her swollen eyes were much disfigured,
And her fair face with tears was foully blubbered.[12]

14

The knight approaching nigh° thus to her said,   *near*
"Fair lady, through foul sorrow ill bedight°,   *afflict*
Great pity is to see you thus dismayed,
And mar the blossom of your beauty bright:
Forthy° appease your grief and heavy plight,   *therefore*
And tell the cause of your conceivéd pain.
For if he live, that hath you doen° despite°,   *done / wrong*
He shall you do due recompense again,
Or else his wrong with greater puissance° maintain."[13]   *strength*

15

Which when she heard, as in despiteful wise,
She willfully her sorrow did augment°,   *increase*
And offered hope of comfort did despise:
Her golden locks most cruelly she rent,
And scratched her face with ghastly dreariment,
Nor would she speak, nor see, nor yet be seen,
But hid her visage, and her head down bent,
Either for grievous shame, or for great teen°,   *grief*
As if her heart with sorrow had transfixed been.[14]

---

11. The "crafty squire" is Archimago. He's referred to as the squire for the next few stanzas.

12. That's a real word. Use it often.

13. I.e., "He'll pay you back or suffer worse for his actions."

14. At the offer of being revenged, she pulls her hair out, scratches her face, and goes silent like a stone. Talk about a temper tantrum.

16

Till her that squire bespake, "Madame my lief°,   *dear*
For God's dear love be not so willful bent,
But do vouchsafe now to receive relief,
The which good fortune doth to you present.
For what boots° it to weep and to waiment°,   *good is / lament*
When ill is chanced, but doth the ill increase,
And the weak mind with double woe torment?"
When she her squire heard speak, she 'gan° appease   *began*
Her voluntary pain, and feel some secret ease.

17

Eftsoone° she said, "Ah gentle trusty Squire,   *presently*
What comfort can I woeful wretch conceive,
Or why should ever I henceforth desire,
To see fair heaven's face, and life not leave,
Since that false traitor did my honor reave°?"   *steal*
"False traitor certes°," said the faerie knight,   *truly*
"I read° the man, that ever would deceive   *say*
A gentle lady, or her wrong through might:
Death were too little pain for such a foul despite.°   *wicked deed*

18

"But now, fair lady, comfort to you make,
And read°, who hath ye wrought this shameful plight.   *say*
That short° revenge the man may overtake,   *quickly*
Where so he be, and soon upon him light."
"Certes°" said she "I wote° not how he hight,°15   *truly / know / is named*
But under him a gray steed did he wield,
Whose sides with dappled circles weren° dight°;   *were / covered*
Upright he rode, and in his silver shield
He bore a bloody cross, that quartered all the field."16

19

"Now by my head," said Guyon, "much I muse,
How that same knight should do so foul amiss,
Or ever gentle damsel so abuse:
For may I boldly say, he surely is

15. I.e., "I don't know what his name is."
16. She describes the knight who dishonored her as a knight with a shield bearing a red cross. Uh-oh. Hold on now, who is this guy? Careful, Guyon.

A right good knight, and true of word unwise:
I present was, and can it witness well,
When arms he swore, and straight did enterprise
The adventure of the Errant Damsel,
In which he hath great glory won, as I hear tell.

20

"Nathless° he shortly shall again be tried,   *nevertheless*
And fairly quit him of the imputed blame,
Else be ye sure he dearly shall abide,
Or make you good amendment for the same:
All wrongs have mends, but no amends of shame.[17]
Now therefore lady, rise out of your pain,
And see the salving° of your blotted name."   *healing*
Full loath° she seemed thereto, but yet did feign°;   *unwilling / pretend*
For she was inly° glad her purpose so to gain.   *on the inside*

21

Her purpose was not such, as she did feign,
Nor yet her person such, as it was seen,
But under simple show and semblant° plain   *secret*
Lurked false Duessa[18] secretly unseen,
As a chaste virgin, that wrongéd been:
So had false Archimago her disguised,
To cloak her guile with sorrow and sad teen°;   *grief*
And eke° himself had craftily devised   *also*
To be her squire, and do her service well aguised°.   *disguised*

22

Her late° forlorn° and naked he had found,   *recently / hopeless*
Where she did wander in waste wilderness,
Lurking in rocks and caves far under ground,[19]
And with green moss covering her nakedness,
To hide her shame and loathly° filthiness;   *wicked*

17. Guyon knows the knight by his shield. It's Redcross of course. Guyon knows he's a faithful knight, but he vows to do a thorough investigation and either prove him innocent or require that he make amends for any wrong doing. The "Errant Damsel" is Una from Book I, for whom Redcross did many daring deeds.

18. Ooooh . . . you should've known. This is no chaste maiden; this is Duessa, the wicked woman from Book I, teaming up with Archimago.

19. She was Gollum's long lost girl friend.

Since her Prince Arthur of proud ornaments
And borrowed beauty spoiled. Her nathless°   *nevertheless*
The enchanter finding fit for his intents,
Did thus revest°, and decked with due habiliments.[20]   *re-clothe*

23

For all he did, was to deceive good knights,
And draw them from pursuit of praise and fame,
To slug in sloth and sensual delights,
And end their days with irrenowned° shame.   *inglorious*
And now exceeding grief him overcame,
To see the Redcross thus advancéd high;
Therefore this crafty engine he did frame,
Against his praise to stir up enmity
Of such, as virtues like mote° unto him ally.[21]   *might*

24

So now he Guyon guides an uncouth way
Through woods and mountains, till they came at last
Into a pleasant dale, that lowly lay
Betwixt two hills, whose high heads over placed,
The valley did with cool shade overcast,
Through midst thereof a little river rolled,
By which there sat a knight with helm unlaced,
Himself refreshing with the liquid cold,
After his travel long, and labors manifold.

25

"Lo yonder he," cried Archimage[22] aloud,
"That wrought the shameful fact, which I did show;
And now he doth himself in secret shroud,
To fly the vengeance for his outrage due;
But vain: for ye shall dearly do him rue°,   *harm*
So God ye speed, and send you good success;
Which we far off will here abide to view."

20. He put some clothes on her.
21. Archimago's chief purpose is to rid good knights of their praiseworthy virtues.
22. "Archimage" is a variant spelling of "Archimago." It is the same character. This variant is used to help the line scan correctly, preserving the iambic meter.

So they him left, inflamed with wrathfulness,
That straight against that knight his spear he did address.[23]

26

Who seeing him from far so fierce to prick°,	*ride*
His warlike arms about him 'gan° embrace,	*began*
And in the rest his ready spear did stick;	
Though when as still he saw him towards pace,	
He 'gan° rencounter° him in equal race.[24]	*began / battle*
They been met, both ready to affrap,°	*strike*
When suddenly that warrior 'gan° abase°	*began / put down*
His threatened spear, as if some new mishap	
Had him betide, or hidden danger did entrap.[25]	

27

And cried, "Mercy sir knight, and mercy Lord,	
For mine offence and heedless hardiment°,	*roughness*
That had almost committed crime abhorred,	
And with reproachful shame mine honor shent°,	*removed*
Whiles cursèd steel against that badge I bent,	
The sacred badge of my Redeemer's death,	
Which on your shield is set for ornament."	
But his fierce foe his steed could stay° uneath°,	*stop / with difficulty*
Who pricked with courage keen, did cruel battle breathe.	

28

But when he heard him speak, straight way he knew	
His error, and himself inclining said;	
"Ah dear Sir Guyon, well becometh you,	
But me behooveth° rather to upbraid,	*ought*
Whose hasty hand so far from reason strayed,[26]	
That almost it did heinous violence	
On that fair image of that heavenly maid,[27]	

23. As soon as Redcross is pointed out to Guyon, he lowers his spear and proceeds to attack.

24. When Redcross sees Guyon galloping across the plain, he hurriedly armors himself, mounts his steed, and proceeds to charge toward Guyon.

25. Just before the knights are to meet, Guyon lowers his spear.

26. I.e., "I would wish you well, but I must rebuke you for your hasty attack." This is Guyon's first lesson in temperance. Temperance is not hasty or wrathful.

27. That's Glorianna, the Faerie Queene, who is also a picture of Queen Elizabeth of England.

That decks and arms your shield with fair defense:
Your courtesy takes on you another's due offense."

29

So been they both at one, and done uprear
Their beavers° bright, each other for to greet;   *face guards*
Goodly comportance° each to other bear,   *greeting*
And entertain themselves with courtesies meet,
Then said the Redcross knight, "Now mote° I weet°,   *might / know*
Sir Guyon, why with so fierce saliance°,   *assault*
And fell intent ye did at erst° me meet;   *first*
For since I know your goodly governance,
Great cause, I ween°, you guided, or some uncouth chance."   *think*

30

"Certes°," said he, "well mote° I shame to tell   *certainly / might*
The fond encheason°, that me hither led.   *foolish reason*
A false infamous faitour° late befell   *villain*
Me for to meet, that seemed ill bested°,   *undone*
And plained° of grievous outrage, which he read°   *showed / explained*
A knight had wrought against a lady gent;
Which to avenge, he to this place me led,
Where you he made the mark of his intent,
And now is fled; foul shame him follow, where he went."

31

So can° he turn his earnest unto game,   *did*
Through goodly handling and wise temperance.
By this his agéd guide in presence came;
Who soon as on that knight his eye did glance,
Eftsoones° of him had perfect cognizance,   *presently*
Since him in Fairy court he late avized°;[28]   *had seen*
And said, "Fair son, God give you happy chance,
And that dear cross upon your shield devised,
Wherewith above all knights ye goodly seem aguised°.   *dressed*

32

"Joy may you have, and everlasting fame,
Of late most hard achievement by you done,
For which enrolléd is your glorious name

---

28. I.e., he realized who he was because he was in the Faerie court recently.

In heavenly registers above the sun,
Where you a saint with saints your seat have won:[29]
But wretched we, where ye have left your mark,
Must now anew begin, like race to run;
God guide thee, Guyon, well to end thy work,
And to the wishéd haven bring thy weary bark°."   *boat*

33

"Palmer," him answered the Redcross knight
"His be the praise, that this achievement wrought,
Who made my hand the organ of his might;
More than goodwill to me attribute naught:
For all I did, I did but as I ought.[30]
But you, fair sir, whose pageant next ensues,
Well mote° ye thee, as well can wish your thought,   *might*
That home ye may report thrice happy news;
For well ye worthy been for worth and gentle thews°."   *manners*

34

So courteous conge° both did give and take,   *farewell*
With right hands plighted,[31] pledges of good will.
Then Guyon forward 'gan° his voyage make,   *began*
With his black Palmer, that him guided still.[32]
Still he him guided over dale and hill,
And with his steady staff did point his way:
His race with reason, and with words his will,
From foul intemperance he oft did stay,
And suffered not in wrath his hasty steps to stray.[33]

35

In this fair wise they traveled long yfere°,   *and far*
Through many hard assays°, which did betide;   *adventures*
Of which he honor still away did bear,

29. The Palmer is praising Redcross for the heroics of Book I.
30. I.e., "Palmer, give praise to God who made my hands. All I did was what I was supposed to do."
31. That's the secret knightly handshake.
32. A palmer is a permanent pilgrim, whose usual attire was a long black robe. A palmer would be a good guide, for he would have made many journeys and would be aware of many dangers.
33. Again, notice the sorts of things that the Palmer is helping Guyon avoid as he learns temperance.

And spread his glory through all countries wide.
At last as chanced them by a forest side
To pass, for succor° from the scorching ray,   *relief*
They heard a rueful° voice, that dernly° cried   *sorrowful / sadly*
With piercing shrieks, and many a doleful lay;
Which to attend, a while their forward steps they stay.

36

"But if that careless heavens," quoth she, "despise
The doom of just revenge, and take delight
To see sad pageants of men's miseries,
As bound by them to live in lives despite°,   *wretched*
Yet can they not warn death from wretched wight°.   *soul*
Come then, come soon, come sweetest death to me,
And take away this long lent loathéd light:
Sharp by thy wounds, but sweet the medicines be,
That long captived souls from weary thraldome° free.[34]   *slavery*

37

"But thou, sweet babe, whom frowning froward fate
Hath made sad witness of thy father's fall,
Since heaven thee deigns to hold in living state,
Long mayest thou live, and better thrive withal,
Then to thy luckless parents did befall:
Live thou, and to thy mother dead attest,
That clear she did from blemish criminal;
Thy little hands embrued° in bleeding breast   *stained*
Lo I for pledges leave. So give me leave to rest."

38

With that a deadly shriek she forth did throw,
That through the wood re-echoéd again,
And after gave a groan so deep and low,
That seemed her tender heart was rent in twain,
Or thrilled with point of thorough piercing pain;
As gentle hind, whose sides with cruél steel
Through launchéd, forth her bleeding life does rain,
Whiles the sad pang approaching she does feel,
Brays out her latest breath, and up her eyes doth seal.

34. Guyon and the Palmer hear a woman (Amavia) shrieking in the woods. She is
cursing heaven for a great grievance and praying for death.

39

Which when that warrior heard, dismounting strait
From his tall steed, he rushed into the thick,
And soon arrivéd, where that sad portrait
Of death and labor lay, half dead, half quick°,   *alive*
In whose white alabaster breast did stick
A cruel knife, that made a grisly wound,
From which forth gushed a stream of gore-blood thick,
That all her goodly garments stained around,
And into a deep sanguine° did the grassy ground.[35]   *red*

40

Pitiful spectacle of deadly smart°,   *pain*
Beside a bubbling fountain low she lay,
Which she increased with her bleeding heart,
And the clean waves with purple gore did ray;
Als° in her lap a lovely babe did play   *also*
His cruel sport, instead of sorrow due;
For in her streaming blood he did embay°   *bathe*
His little hands, and tender joints imbrue°;   *soak*
Pitiful spectacle, as ever eye did view.[36]

41

Besides them both, upon the soiled grass
The dead corpse of an arméd knight was spread,
Whose armor all with blood besprinkled was;
His ruddy lips did smile, and rosy red
Did paint his cheerful cheeks, yet being dead,
Seeméd to have been a goodly personage,
Now in his freshest flower of lusty head,
Fit to inflame fair lady with love's rage,
But that fierce fate did crop the blossom of his age.[37]

42

Whom when the good Sir Guyon did behold,
His heart 'gan° wax° as stark, as marble stone,   *began / grow / stiff*

---

35. Guyon, upon hearing the screams, rushes into the woods. There he finds a woman (Amavia) who has just stabbed herself with a knife and is bleeding.

36. Guyon also finds a baby lying next to the bleeding woman. But instead of being sad, the baby is happily splashing in his mother's blood.

37. Beside the woman and the baby lies the corpse of a strong, good looking knight.

And his fresh blood did freeze with fearful cold,
That all his senses seemed bereft atone°:   *at once*
At last his mighty ghost 'gan° deep to groan,   *began*
As lion grudging in his great disdain,
Mourns inwardly, and makes to himself moan:
Till ruth° and frail affection did constrain,   *misery*
His stout courage to stoop, and show his inward pain.

43

Out of her goréd wound the cruel steel
He lightly snatched, and did the floodgate stop
With his fair garment: then 'gan° softly feel   *began*
Her feeble pulse, to prove if any drop
Of living blood yet in her veins did hop;
Which when he felt to move, he hopéd fair
To call back life to her forsaken shop;
So well he did her deadly wounds repair,
That at the last she 'gan° to breath out living air.[38]   *began*

44

Which he perceiving greatly 'gan° rejoice,   *began*
And goodly counsel, that for wounded heart
Is meetest° medicine, tempered with sweet voice;[39]   *best*
"Ay me, dear lady, which the image art
Of rueful pity, and impatient smart,
What direful chance, arméd with revenging fate,
Or curséd hand hath played this cruel part,
Thus foul to hasten your untimely date;
Speak, O dear lady, speak: help never comes too late."

45

Therewith her dim eyelids she up 'gan° rear,   *began*
On which the dreary death did sit, as sad
As lump of lead, and made dark clouds appear;
But when as him all in bright armor clad
Before her standing she espiéd° had,   *seeing*
As one out of a deadly dream affright,

38. Guyon pulls the dagger from her chest and stops the wound. He is also able to feel a pulse, and soon she begins breathing again.

39. Guyon is quite pleased with the progress the woman is making. He decides the best medicine for the moment is good counsel.

She weakly started, yet she nothing dread:
Straight down again her self in great despite
She groveling threw to ground, as hating life and light.

46

The gentle knight her soon with careful pain
Uplifted light, and softly did uphold:
Thrice he her reared°, and thrice she sunk again,   *raised*
Till he his arms about her sides 'gan° fold,   *began*
And to her said; "Yet if the stony cold
Have not all seized on your frozen heart,
Let one word fall that may your grief unfold,
And tell the secret of your mortal smart°;   *hurt*
He oft finds present help, who does his grief impart."[40]

47

Then casting up a deadly look, full low,
She sighed from bottom of her wounded breast,
And after, many bitter throbs did throw
With lips full pale and faltering tongue oppressed,
These words she breathéd forth from riven chest;
"Leave, ah leave off, what ever wight° thou be,   *creature*
To let a weary wretch from her due rest,
And trouble dying soul's tranquility.
Take not away now got, which none would give to me."[41]

48

"Ah far be it," said he, "Dear dame for me,
To hinder soul from her desired rest,
Or hold sad life in long captivity:
For all I seek, is but to have redressed
The bitter pangs, that doth your heart infest.
Tell then, O lady tell, what fatal prief°   *trial*
Hath with so huge misfortune you oppressed?
That I may cast to compass your relief,
Or die with you in sorrow, and partake your grief."[42]

40. I.e., "If you can still speak, give me some explanation of your situation. Tell me what's wrong; maybe I can help."

41. I.e., "Leave a dying woman alone. Let me have the rest that no one has ever given me."

42. Guyon assures Amavia that he isn't trying to interrupt her rest. He just wants to know how he can "redress the wrongs" that afflict her soul or else die from grief with her. What a man, that Guyon.

49

With feeble hands then stretchéd forth on high,
As heaven accusing guilty of her death,
And with dry drops congealed° in her eye,   *solidified*
In these sad words she spent her utmost breath:
"Hear then, O man, the sorrows that uneath°   *hardly*
My tongue can tell, so far all sense they pass:
Lo this dead corpse, that lies here underneath,
The gentlest knight, that ever on green grass
Gay steed with spurs did prick°, the good Sir Mordant was.   *ride*

50

"Was, aye the while, that he is not so now
My lord my love; my dear lord, my dear love,
So long as heaven's just with equal brow
Vouchsaféd to behold us from above,
One day when him high courage did emmove°,   *motivate*
As want ye knights to seek adventures wild,
He prickéd° forth, his puissant° force to prove,   *rode / strong*
Me then he left enwombéd° of this child,   *pregnant*
This luckless child, whom thus ye see with blood defiled.⁴³

51

"Him fortuned, hard fortune ye may guess,
To come, where vile Acrasia does won°,   *live*
Acrasia, a false enchantress,
That many errant knights hath foul fordone°:   *destroyed*
Within a wandering island, that doth run
And stray in perilous gulf, her dwelling is:
Fair sir, if ever there ye travel, shun
The curséd land where many wend amiss°,   *go astray*
And know it by the name; it hight° the Bower of Bliss.⁴⁴   *is called*

52

"Her bliss is all in pleasure and delight,
Wherewith she makes her lovers drunken mad,
And then with words and weeds° of wondrous might,   *herbs*
On them she works her will to uses bad:
My lifest° lord she thus beguiled had;   *dearest*

43. Amavia is telling Guyon her story: Sir Mordant was Amavia's husband, and he went in search of adventures while Amavia stayed home pregnant.
44. Sir Mordant encountered Acrasia, a wicked witch who inhabits the Bower of Bliss.

For he was flesh: all flesh doth frailty breed.
Whom when I heard to been so ill bestad°,   *situated*
Weak wretch I wrapped myself in palmer's weed°,   *garments*
And cast to seek him forth through danger and great dread.

53

"Now had fair Cynthia by even turns
Full measured three quarters of her year,
And thrice three times had filled her crooked horns,[45]
Whenas my womb her burden would forbear,
And bade me call Lucina to me near.
Lucina came: a man-child forth I brought:[46]
The woods, the nymphs, my bowers, my midwives were,
Hard help at need. So dear thee babe I bought,
Yet naught too dear I deemed, while so my dear I sought.

54

"Him so I sought, and so at last I found
Where him that witch had thrallèd° to her will,   *enslaved*
In chains of lust and lewd° desires bound,   *indecent*
And so transformèd from his former skill,
That me he knew not, neither his own ill;
Till through wise handling and fair governance,
I him recured° to a better will,   *recovered*
Purged from drugs of foul intemperance:[47]
Then means I 'gan° devise for his deliverance.   *began*

55

"Which when the vile enchantress perceivèd,
How that my lord from her I would reprieve°,   *release*
With cup thus charmed, him parting she deceived:
'Sad verse, give death to him that death does give,
And loss of love, to her that loves to live,
So soon as Bacchus with the Nymph does link.'

45. Cynthia (or Artemis) was the Greek goddess of the hunt and the moon. Thus "three quarters of a year" or "thrice three times" would give us the grand total of nine months. The "crooked horns" are the phases of the moon.

46. Lucina was a goddess of childbirth and motorcycles. At any rate, while she was on her way to rescue her husband from Acrasia, she gave birth to a son.

47. This description sets Guyon at odds with the witch Acrasia and her Bower of Bliss. (Even Acrasia's name means "intemperance.") He is the Knight of Temperance; he battles all that is intemperate.

So parted we and on our journey drive,
Till coming to this well, he stooped to drink:
The charm fulfilled, dead suddenly he down did sink.⁴⁸

56

"Which when I wretch . . ." Not one word more she said
But breaking off, the end for want of breath,
And sliding soft, as down to sleep her laid,
And ended all her woe in quiet death.⁴⁹
That seeing good Sir Guyon, could uneath°   *hardly*
From tears abstain, for grief his heart did grate,
And from so heavy sight his head did wreath°,   *turn*
Accusing fortune, and too cruél fate,
Which plungéd had fair lady in so wretched state.

57

Then turning to his Palmer said, "Old sire
Behold the image of mortality,
And feeble nature clothed with fleshly tire°,   *garments*
When raging passion with fierce tyranny
Robs reason of her due regality°   *majesty*
And makes it servant to her basest part:
The strong it weakens with infirmity,
And with bold fury arms the weakest heart;
The strong through pleasure soonest falls, the weak through smart°."⁵⁰ *pain*

58

"But temperance," said he with golden squire°,⁵¹   *square*
"Betwixt them both can measure out a mean,
Neither to melt in pleasure's hot desire,
Nor fry in heartless grief and doleful teen°.   *misery*
Thrice happy man, who fares them both atween°:   *between*
But since this wretched woman overcome
Of anguish, rather than of crime hath been,

48. The witch cast a spell on a cup, and when he stopped to drink at the stream where they are now, he immediately fell down dead.
49. That's one long gasp of breath.
50. Guyon says that "fierce passion" is a tyrant. It is an abusive ruler that destroys lives through pain and pleasure.
51. Squire means "square"—as in the measuring device. The square was often used in art work to symbolize the virtue temperance. The Palmer speaks with "golden measure."

Reserve her cause to her eternal doom,
And in the mean° vouchsafe her honorable tomb."⁵²   *meantime*

59

"Palmer," quoth he, "death is an equal doom
To good and bad, the common inn of rest;
But after death the trial is to come,
When best shall be to them, that lived best:
But both alike, when death hath both suppressed,
Religious reverence doth burial teen°,   *require*
Which who so wants, wants so much of his rest;
For all so great shame after death I ween°,   *suppose*
As self to dying bad, unburied bad to been."⁵³

60

So both agree their bodies to engrave°;   *bury*
The great earth's womb they open to the sky,
And with sad cypress seemly it embrave°,   *decorate*
Then covering with a clod° their closéd eye,   *lump of dirt*
They lay therein those corpses tenderly,
And bid them sleep in everlasting peace.
But ere they did their utmost obsequy°,   *funeral rites*
Sir Guyon more affection to increase,
Benempt° a sacred vow, which none should aye° release.   *swore / ever*

61

The dead knight's sword out of his sheath he drew,
With which he cut a lock of all their hair,
Which meddling with their blood and earth, he threw
Into the grave, and gan devoutly swear;
"Such and such evil God on Guyon rear°,   *bring*
And worse and worse young orphan be thy pain,

52. Temperance, the Palmer says, is able to steer a middle ground between "fierce passion" and "heartless grief." He also says she's worthy of burial.

53. Guyon says that it's just as bad to die and be unburied as it is to die badly to begin. What's the big deal? What does "shame" and "rest" have to do with being buried? Is this merely ancient paganism or is this Christian? Guyon understands that Christian burial looks in faith to the resurrection of the body: We bury bodies because they are like seeds. New and glorious bodies will one day rise from them (1 Cor. 15:35–44).

If I or thou due vengeance do forbear°,   *give up*
Till guilty blood her guerdon° do obtain":[54]   *ransom*
So shedding many tears, they closed the earth again.

54. Guyon cuts hair from each of the victims, dips it in their blood, and casts it into the grave vowing to revenge the evil that has destroyed this family. This provides the thematic cause of Guyon's mission and gives greater definition to his quest. His mission: to seek out and destroy Acrasia and her Bower of Bliss.

 Bury the Batchet

Directions: Identify where in the story the following quotes came from. Explain what they mean and their significance to the story.

1. "Fair son of Mars, that seek with warlike spoil.
   And great achievements great yourself to make,
   Vouchsafe to stay your steed for humble miser's sake."

2. "So courteous conge both did give and take,
   With right hands plighted, pledges of good will."

3. "Her bliss is all in pleasure and delight,
   Wherewith she makes her lovers drunken mad."

Canto II.

Babe's bloody hands may not be cleansed,
the face of Golden Mean.
Her sisters, two Extremities:
strive her to banish clean.

1

Thus when Sir Guyon with his faithful guide	
Had with due rites and dolorous° lament	*sad*
The end of their sad tragedy up-tied,	
The little babe up in his arms he hent°;	*took*
Who with sweet pleasance and bold blandishment	
'Gan° smile on them, that rather ought to weep,	*began*
As careless of his woe, or innocent	
Of that was doen°, that ruth° empiercéd° deep	*happening / pity / pierced*
In that knight's heart, and words with bitter tears did steep.[1]	

2

"Ah luckless babe, born under cruél star,	
And in dead parents' baleful ashes bred,	
Full little weenest° thou, what sorrows are	*know*
Left thee for portion of thy livelihood,[2]	
Poor orphan in the wide world scattered,	
As budding branch rent from the native tree,	

---

1. You know, like tea.
2. I.e., "You hardly know the sorrows that await you in your life."

And thrown forth, till it be withered:
Such is the state of men: thus enter we
Into this life with woe, and end with misery."

3

Then soft himself inclining on his knee
Down to that well, did in the water ween°   *think*
(So love does loath disdainful nicety)[3]
His guilty hands from bloody gore to clean,
He washed them oft and oft°, yet not they been   *over and over*
For all his washing cleaner. Still he strove,
Yet still the little hands were bloody seen;
The which him into great amazement drove,
And into diverse doubt his wavering wonder clove°.[4]   *cut in two*

4

He wist° not whether blot of foul offence   *knew*
Might not be purged with water nor with bath;
Or that high God, in lieu of innocence,
Imprinted had that token of his wrath,
To show how sore blood-guiltiness he hateth;
Or that the charm and venom, which they drunk,
Their blood with secret filth infected hath,
Being diffused through the senseless trunk,
That through the great contagion° direful deadly stunk.[5]   *transmitting disease*

5

Whom thus at gaze, the Palmer 'gan° to board°   *began / speak to*
With goodly reason, and thus fair bespake;
"Ye been right hard amated°, gracious lord,   *confused*
And of your ignorance great marvel make,
Whiles cause not well conceived ye mistake.

3. He's thinking about why he stated the facts so harshly. I.e., Love hates soft words that are spoken simply for vain comfort.

4. Guyon takes the child to the stream and attempts to wash off the blood, but though he tries many times, the blood won't be removed.

5. Guyon can't figure out if a) the offense was so bad that the blood won't come off, b) God's anger burned and fastened the blood to the child as a sign, or c) the potion that killed Sir Mordant had done something weird to his blood. This is one of Spenser's pictures of "Original Sin," the Christian doctrine that teaches that sin has been passed down since Adam from generation to generation (like blood) as a "natural" inclination.

But know, that secret virtues[6] are infused
In every fountain, and in every lake,
Which who hath skill them rightly to have choosed,
To proof of passing wonders hath full often used.

6

"Of those some were so from their source endued
By great Dame Nature, from whose fruitful pap°   *breast*
Their wellheads spring, and are with moisture dewed;
Which feeds each living plant with liquid sap,
And fills with flowers fair Flora's[7] painted lap:
But other some by gift of later grace,
Or by good prayers, or by other hap°,   *happening*
Had virtue poured into their water's base,
And thenceforth were renowned, and sought from place to place.[8]

7

"Such is this well, wrought by occasion strange,
Which to her nymph befell. Upon a day,
As she the woods with bow and shafts did range,
The heartless hind° and roebuck° to dismay,   *female deer / male deer*
Dan° Faunus[9] chanced to meet her by the way,   *sir*
And kindling fire at her fair burning eye,
Inflaméd was to follow beauty's chase,
And chaséd her, that fast from him did fly;
As hind from her, so she fled from her enemy.[10]

8

"At last when failing breath began to faint,
And saw no means to scape°, of shame afraid,   *escape*
She set her down to weep for sore° constraint°,   *bitter / frustration*

6. "Virtue" here doesn't refer to good morals. Virtue in the old world was more akin to "power" or "heavenly being" and often referred to spirits or angels. This point is made by the story he tells.

7. She was the goddess of flowers.

8. The Palmer tells Guyon that all of nature is infused with various "virtues" either naturally or through other means. He's about to tell Guyon what happened to this stream that makes it unable to cleanse the bloody child.

9. This fellow is from Roman myth, a satyr god of nature otherwise known as "El Kissyface."

10. Palmer tells Guyon that once there was a nymph who was chased by El Kissyface.

And to Diana[11] calling loud for aid,
Her dear besought, to let her die a maid°.   *virgin*
The goddess heard, and sudden where she sat,
Welling out streams of tears, and quite dismayed
With stony fear of that rude rustic mate,
Transformed her to a stone from steadfast virgin's state.[12]

9
"Lo now she is that stone, from whose two heads,
As from two weeping eyes, fresh streams do flow,
Yet cold through fear, and old conceived dreads;
And yet the stone her semblance seems to show,
Shaped like a maid, that such ye may her know;
And yet her virtues in her water bide°:   *remain*
For it is chaste and pure, as purest snow,
Nor lets her waves with any filth be died,
But ever like her self unstained hath been tried.[13]

10
"From thence it comes, that this babe's bloody hand
May not be cleansed with water of this well:
Nor certes°, sir, strive you it to withstand,   *truly*
But let them still be bloody, as befell,
That they his mother's innocence may tell,[14]
As she bequeathed in her last testament;
That as a sacred symbol it may dwell
In her son's flesh, to mind° revengement°,   *remind / revenge*
And be for all chaste dames an endless monument."[15]

11. She's the goddess of chastity, hunting, and video games.

12. So Diana heard the nymph's plea and changed her into stone, thereby preserving her chastity. This nymph-stone marks the spring of this very stream and carries the qualities of the nymph's request.

13. And that's why the water cannot be tainted by the blood that stains the infant. It's pure and undefiled due to Diana's spell.

14. The Palmer says that the child's blood stained hands are signs of his mother's innocence, and they remind all who see them of the need for justice.

15. Elizabeth Heale points out that Spenser brings both stories together comparing Amavia and the petrified nymph as "chaste dames." Both of these women pray to heaven and die, but an "endless monument" is erected for each: blood stained hands and a pure stream.

11

He hearkened to his reason, and the child
Up taking, to the Palmer gave to bear;
But his sad father's arms with blood defiled,
An heavy load himself did lightly rear,
And turning to that place, in which whylere°   *before*
He left his lofty steed with golden sell°,   *saddle*
And goodly gorgeous barbs°, him found not there.   *armor*
By other accident that earst° befell,   *ever*
He is conveyed, but how or where, here fits not tell.[16]

12

Which when Sir Guyon saw, all were he wroth°,   *angry*
Yet algates° must he soft himself appease,[17]   *regardless*
And fairly fare° on foot, how ever loath°;   *go / upset*
His double burden[18] did him sore disease.
So long they travailed° with little ease,   *labored*
Till that at last they to a castle came,
Built on a rock adjoining to the seas:
It was an ancient work of antique fame,
And wondrous strong by nature, and by skillful frame.[19]

13

Therein three sisters dwelt of sundry° sort,   *different*
The children of one sire by mothers three;
Who dying whylome° did divide this fort   *sometime before*
To them by equal shares in equal fee:
But strifeful mind, and diverse quality
Drew them in parts, and each made others foe;
Still did they strive, and daily disagree;
The eldest did against the youngest go,
And both against the middest° meant to worken° woe.[20]   *middle / work*

16. Someone has stolen Guyon's horse and armor. But Spenser will tell us about that later.

17. I.e., however he felt, he had to pull himself together.

18. The "double burden" can refer figuratively to the events surrounding Amavia and Guyon's stolen horse, or merely to the fact that they are carrying both a child and Mordant's armor, or both.

19. Guyon, the Palmer, and the child come to a castle built on rock by the sea.

20. Three sisters live in the castle and apparently do not get along very well.

14

Where when the knight arrived, he was right well
Received, as knight of so much worth became,
Of second sister, who did far excel
The other two; Medina was her name,
A sober sad, and comely courteous dame;
Who rich arrayed, and yet in modest guise,
In goodly garments, that her well became,
Fair marching forth in honorable wise,
Him at the threshold met, and well did enterprise.

15

She led him up into a goodly bower°,   *inner room*
And comely courted° with meet° modesty,   *cared for / fitting*
Nor in her speech, nor in her havior°,   *behavior*
Was lightness seen, or looser vanity,
But gracious womanhood, and gravity,
Above the reason of her youthly years:
Her golden locks she roundly did up-tie
In breaded trammels°, that no looser hairs   *locks*
Did out of order stray about her dainty ears.[21]

16

Whilst she her self thus busily did frame,
Seemly to entertain her new-come guest,
News hereof to her other sisters came,
Who all this while were at their wanton rest,
According each her friend with lavish feast:
They were two knights of peerless puissance°,   *strength*
And famous far abroad for warlike gest°,   *deed*
Which to these ladies love did countenance°,   *show*
And to his mistress each himself strove to advance.

17

He that made° love unto the eldest dame,   *showed*
Was hight° Sir Huddibras, an hardy man;   *named*
Yet not so good of deeds, as great of name,
Which he by many rash adventures wan°,   *won*
Since errant arms to sue° he first began;   *pursue*
More huge in strength, than wise in works he was,

21. "Dainty ears." Golly. Medina is the middle sister. She is all grace and charm, and she meets Guyon and company with great hospitality.

And reason with fool-hardice° over ran;   *fool-hardy*
Stern melancholy did his courage pass°,   *surpass*
And was for terror more, all armed in shining brass.[22]

18

But he that loved the youngest, was Sansloy,
He that fair Una late foul outraged,
The most unruly, and the boldest boy,
That ever warlike weapons managéd,
And to all lawless lust encouragéd,
Through strong opinion of his matchless might:
Nor ought he cared, whom he endamagéd°   *hurt*
By tortuous wrong, or whom bereaved of right.
He now this lady's champion chose for love to fight.[23]

19

These two gay knights, vowed to so diverse loves,
Each other does envy with deadly hate,
And daily war against his foe-man moves,
In hope to win more favor with his mate,
And the other's pleasing service to abate,
To magnify his own.[24] But when they heard,
How in that place strange knight arrivéd late,
Both knights and ladies forth right angry fared,
And fiercely unto battle stern themselves prepared.[25]

20

But ere° they could proceed unto the place,   *before*
Where he abode, themselves at discord fell,
And cruel combat joined in middle space:

22. The oldest sister is loved by a fool named Sir Huddibras. This fellow just happened to be big enough to get out of most scrapes by looking kind of scary with all his armor on.

23. The youngest sister is loved by Sansloy, a character, you may recall, who we met in Book I. Sansloy is brave and fierce, but he is thoughtless and wicked at heart.

24. Sansloy and Huddibras are nearly always fighting in order to show off. They want to win greater admiration in the eyes of their girls and spoil the reputation of the other.

25. As soon as the oldest and youngest sister and their knights hear there is a new knight in the castle, they hurry out ready to fight each other again. They see this new knight as a threat to their reputations. Perhaps they are fighting for the right to fight the new knight. Perhaps they are fighting for the right to befriend the new knight. Perhaps they are fighting because they cannot agree on a proper greeting. Everything is a threat to them. So for these two fools, everything is worth fighting over.

With horrible assault, and fury fell,
They heaped huge strokes, the scornéd life to quell,
That all on uproar from her settled seat
The house was raised, and all that in did dwell;
Seemed that loud thunder with amazement great
Did rend the rattling skies with flames of fouldering° heat.   *thundering*

21

The noise thereof called forth that stranger knight,
To weet°, what dreadful thing was there in hand;   *find out*
Where when as two brave knights in bloody fight
With deadly rancor° he enragéd found,   *resentment*
His sun-broad shield about his wrist he bound,
And shining blade unsheathed, with which he ran
Unto that stead, their strife to understand;
And at his first arrival, them began
With goodly means to pacify°, well as he can.   *make peace*

22

But they him spying, both with greedy force
At once upon him ran, and him beset
With strokes of mortal steel without remorse,
And on his shield like iron sledges beat:
As when a bear and tiger being met
In cruél fight on Lybic Ocean wide,
Espy° a traveler with feet surbet°,   *see / bruised*
Whom they in equal pray hope to divide,
They stint° their strife, and him assail on every side.   *pause*

23

But he, not like a weary traveler,
Their sharp assault right boldly did rebut,
And suffered not their blows to bite him near
But with redoubled buffs them back did put:
Whose grievéd minds, which choler° did englut°,   *anger / fill*
Against themselves turning their wrathful spite,
'Gan° with new rage their shields to hew and cut;   *began*
But still when Guyon came to part their fight,
With heavy load on him they freshly 'gan° to smite.[26]   *began*

26. Guyon, when he sees Sansloy and Huddibras fighting, arms himself and tries to convince them to stop fighting. But this only makes them more angry and they begin to attack Guyon. Guyon takes their strokes well and even deals out a good many of his own. The battle veers back and forth between the three. At points, Huddibras and Sansloy team up to attack Guyon, and at other points, they resume their own battle.

24

As a tall ship tossed in troublous seas,
Whom raging winds threatening to make the prey
Of the rough rocks, do diversely disease,
Meets two contrary billows by the way,
That her on either side do sore assay°,   *attack*
And boast to swallow her in greedy grave;
She scorning both their spites, does make wide way,
And with her breast breaking the foamy wave,
Does ride on both their backs, and fair herself doth save.[27]

25

So boldly he him bears, and rusheth forth
Between them both, by conduct of his blade.
Wondrous great prowess and heroic worth
He showed that day, and rare ensample° made,   *example*
When two so mighty warriors he dismayed:
At once he wards and strikes, he takes and pays,
Now first to yield, now forcing to invade,
Before, behind, and round about him lays:
So double was his pains, so double be his praise.

26

Strange sort of fight, three valiant knights to see
Three combats join in one, and to derrain°   *engage in*
A triple war with triple enmity,
All for their ladies' froward° love to gain,   *contrary*
Which gotten was but hate. So love does reign
In stoutest minds, and maketh monstrous war;
He maketh war, he maketh peace again,
And yet his peace is but continual jar:
O miserable men, that to him subject are.[28]

27

Whilst thus they mingled were in furious arms,
The fair Medina with her tresses° torn,[29]   *hair*
And naked breast, in pity of their harms,
Amongst them ran, and falling them before,

27. Here's one of Spenser's larger similes, comparing Guyon to a ship in storm.
28. These fellas think they're fighting for love. But a fight that is merely for human love is neverending. Such love is a cruel taskmaster. Its peace is a "continual jar." Love must have an ultimate object, namely God, who is love.
29. This means Medina's hair has come undone or unbraided.

Besought them by the womb, which them had born,
And by the loves, which were to them most dear,
And by the knighthood, which they sure had sworn,
Their deadly cruel discord to forbear,
And to her just conditions of fair peace to hear.[30]

28

But her two other sisters standing by,
Her loud gainsaid°, and both their champions bad°   *spoke against / encouraged*
Pursue the end of their strong enmity,
As ever of their loves they would be glad.
Yet she with pithy° words and counsel sad,   *wise*
Still strove their stubborn rages to revoke,
That at the last suppressing fury mad,
They 'gan abstain from dint° of direful stroke,   *blow*
And hearken to the sober speeches, which she spoke.[31]

29

"Ah puissant° lords, what curséd evil sprite°,   *powerful / spirit*
Or fell° Erinys,[32] in your noble hearts   *wicked*
Her hellish brand hath kindled with despite,
And stirred you up to work your willful smarts°?   *wounds*
Is this the joy of arms? Be these the parts
Of glorious knighthood, after blood to thrust,
And not regard due right and just deserts?
Vain is the vaunt, and victory unjust,
That more to mighty hands than rightful cause doth trust.[33]

30

"And were there rightful cause of difference,
Yet were not better, fair it to accord,
Than with blood guiltiness to heap offence,
And mortal vengeance join to crime abhorred?
O fly from wrath, fly, O my liefest° lord: *dearest*

30. Guyon's efforts, though courageous, are useless. Medina finally runs out into the fray and appeals to their mothers, their loves, and their knighthood to stop fighting.

31. Though Guyon is praised for his bravery, his sword cannot bring the peace he had hoped. Thus Spenser teaches us that temperance is brave and fierce, but it must use wisdom and modesty. Medina's sisters would prefer that the knights fight it out, but Medina's chosen words end the strife. She is the personification of wisdom and modesty.

32. These are irrational spirits of anger, also known as the Furies or Eumenides.

33. In other words, the meaning of knighthood isn't simply fighting and bloodshed. A just cause is more important than big muscles and sharp swords.

Sad be the sights, and bitter fruits of war,
And thousand furies wait on wrathful sword;
Nor ought the praise of prowess more doth mar,
Than foul revenging rage, and base contentious jar.[34]

31

"But lovely concord, and most sacred peace
Doth nourish virtue, and fast friendship breeds;
Weak she makes strong and strong thing does increase,
Till it the pitch of highest praise exceeds:
Brave be her wars, and honorable deeds,
By which she triumphs over ire° and pride,   *wrath*
And wins an olive garland for her meeds°:   *wages*
Be therefore, O my dear lords, pacified,
And this mis-seeming° discord meekly lay aside."   *improper*

32

Her gracious words their rancor° did appall,   *fury*
And sunk so deep into their boiling breasts,
That down they let their cruel weapons fall,
And lowly did abase their lofty crests[35]
To her fair presence, and discrete behests.
Then she began a treaty to procure,
And 'stablish terms betwixt both their requests,
That as a law forever should endure;
Which to observe in word of knights they did assure.[36]

33

Which to confirm, and fast to bind their league,
After their weary sweat and bloody toil,
She them besought, during their quiet treague°,   *truce*
Into her lodging to repair a while,
To rest themselves, and grace to reconcile.[37]
They soon consent: so forth with her they fare,

34. I.e., "And even if you have a good reason to be swinging your swords around so madly, you lose your integrity by fighting with wrath and blind anger."

35. They took off their helmets.

36. Medina not only secures a temporary peace, but she negotiates a treaty and they agree to be at peace with each other from that point on.

37. Medina invites the knights and their ladies to a banquet where they can rest and seal their peace with one another. A meal is a common (as here) and a sacred (as in the Eucharist) sign of grateful unity.

Where they are well received, and made to spoil°   *take off*
Themselves of soiled arms, and to prepare
Their minds to pleasure and their mouths to dainty fare.

34

And those two froward sisters, their fair loves
Came with them eke°, all were they wondrous loath°,   *also / annoyed*
And feigned° cheer, as for the time behooves°,   *pretending / requires*
But could not color yet so well the troth°,   *truth*
But that their natures bad appeared in both:
For both did at their second sister grutch°,   *complain*
And inly° grieve, as doth an hidden moth   *on the inside*
The inner garment fret, not the utter° touch;   *outer*
One thought their cheer too little, the other thought too much.[38]

35

Elissa (so the eldest hight°) did deem   *was named*
Such entertainment base, nor ought would eat,
Nor ought would speak, but evermore did seem
As discontent for want of mirth or meat;
No solace could her paramour° entreat,   *lover*
Her once to show, nor court, nor dalliance°,   *flirting*
But with bent lowering brows, as she would threat,
She scowled, and frowned with froward countenance,
Unworthy of fair ladies' comely governance°.[39]   *behavior*

36

But young Perissa was of other mind,
Full of disport, still laughing, loosely light,
And quite contrary to her sister's kind;
No measure in her mood, no rule of right,
But poured out in pleasure and delight;
In wine and meats she flowed above the bank,
And in excess exceeded her own might;
In sumptuous tire she joyed herself to prank,
But of her love too lavish little have she thank.[40]

38. The oldest and youngest sisters attempt to be polite and cheerful, but their inner character is only too obvious.

39. Elissa, the oldest sister, is a frump. She's sour, serious, and boring, like far too many Christians.

40. Perissa, the youngest sister, is a ditz.

37

Fast by her side did sit the bold Sansloy
Fit mate for such a mincing minion,
Who in her looseness took exceeding joy;
Might not be found a franker franion°,   *loose fellow*
Of her lewd° parts° to make companion;   *immoral / activities*
But Huddibras, more like a malcontent°,   *crank*
Did see and grieve at his bold fashion;
Hardly could he endure his hardiment,
Yet still he sat, and inly° did himself torment.[41]   *on the inside*

38

Betwixt them both the fair Medina sat
With sober grace, and goodly carriage:
With equal measure she did moderate
The strong extremities of their outrage;
That forward pair she ever would assuage,
When they would strive due reason to exceed;
But that same froward twain would accourage°,   *encourage*
And of her plenty add unto their need:
So kept she them in order, and herself in heed.

39

Thus fairly she a'temperéd° her feast,   *fashioned*
And pleased them all with meet satiety°,   *fullness*
At last when lust of meat and drink was ceased,
She Guyon dear besought of courtesy,
To tell from whence he came through jeopardy,
And whither now on new adventure bound.
Who with bold grace, and comely gravity,
Drawing to him the eyes of all around,
From lofty siege began these words aloud to sound.[42]

40

"This thy demand, O lady, doth revive
Fresh memory in me of that great Queen,
Great and most glorious virgin Queen alive,
That with her sovereign power, and scepter shine

41. Sansloy gets along just fine with Perissa's looseness. Like many cowards, Huddibras is only brave enough to turn red and sputter.

42. After Medina has filled everyone to full, she asks Guyon where he has come from and where he is going.

All Faerie Land does peaceable sustain.[43]
In widest ocean she her throne does rear,
That over all the earth it may be seen;
As morning sun her beams dispreaden° clear,   *spread out*
And in her face fair peace and mercy doth appear.

41

"In her the riches of all heavenly grace
In chief degree are heaped up on high:
And all that else this world's enclosure base,
Hath great or glorious in mortal eye.
Adorns the person of her majesty;
That men beholding so great excellence,
And rare perfection in mortality,
Do her adore with sacred reverence,
As the idol° of her Maker's great magnificence.   *symbol*

42

"To her I homage and my service owe,
In number of the noblest knights on ground,
'Mongst whom on me she deigned to bestow
Order of Maydenhead, the most renowned,
That may this day in all the world be found:
An yearly solemn feast she wants to make
The day that first doth lead the year around;[44]
To which all knights of worth and courage bold
Resort, to hear of strange adventures to be told.

43

"There this old Palmer showed himself that day,
And to that mighty princess did complain
Of grievous mischiefs, which a wicked fay°   *fairy*
Had wrought, and many whelmed° in deadly pain,   *overwhelmed*
Whereof he craved redress°. My sovereign,   *vengeance*
Whose glory is in gracious deeds, and joys
Throughout the world her mercy to maintain,
Eftsoons° devised redress for such annoys;   *quickly*
Me all unfit for so great purpose she employs.[45]

43. This "Queen" is of course the Faerie Queene and all that she represents.

44. The New Year commenced right after Easter in the Middle Ages, usually sometime in March.

45. Guyon says that it all started on New Year's, when the Palmer showed up to the court of the Faerie Queene to acquaint her with the deeds of a wicked sorceress. After hearing the plea, the Faerie Queene sent Guyon on the quest.

44

"Now hath fair Phoebe⁴⁶ with her silver face
Thrice seen the shadows of the nether world,
Since last I left that honorable place,⁴⁷
In which her royal presence is introlled°;   *enthroned*
Nor ever shall I rest in house nor hold,
Till I that false Acrasia have won;
Of whose foul deeds, too hideous to be told
I witness am and this their wretched son,
Whose woeful parents she hath wickedly fordone°."⁴⁸   *ruined*

45

"Tell on, fair sir," said she, "that doleful tale,
From which sad ruth° does seem you to restrain,   *pity*
That we may pity such unhappy bale°,   *evil-doing*
And learn from pleasure's poison to abstain:
Ill by ensample good doth often gain."
Then forward he his purpose 'gan pursue,
And told the story of the mortal pain,
Which Mordant and Amavia did rue°;   *regret*
As with lamenting eyes himself did lately view.⁴⁹

46

Night was far spent, and now in ocean deep
Orion, flying fast from hissing snake,
His flaming head did hasten for to steep°,⁵⁰   *soak*
When of his piteous tale he end did make;
Whilst with delight of that he wisely spake,
Those guests beguiled, did beguile their eyes
Of kindly sleep that did them overtake.
At last when they had marked the chargéd skies,
They wist° their hour was spent; each to rest him hies°.   *knew / hastens*

46. Phoebe was originally a Titaness who came to be associated with the goddess Artemis and eventually (as here) the moon.

47. You can do the math, but that's about three months, placing this episode smack dab in the middle of the summer around the summer solstice.

48. Guyon adds that he is also the witness of the deeds of this witch, Acrasia. For it was she who destroyed the family of Amavia and Sir Mordant, leaving the small child in Guyon's care.

49. Guyon goes on and tells the whole tale of Amavia and Mordant.

50. The constellations flying through the sky show how late it is.

Off to Bed with You

Directions: Identify where in the story the following quotes came from. Explain what they mean and their significance to the story.

1. "The eldest did against the youngest go,
   And both against the middest meant to worken woe."

2. "So double was his pains, so double be his praise."

3. "That with her sovereign power, and scepter shine
   All Faerie Land does peaceable sustain."

Canto III.

Vain Braggadochio getting Guyon's
horse is made the scorn
Of knighthood true, and is of fair
Belphoebe fowl forlorn.

1

Soon as the morrow fair with purple beams	
Dispersed the shadows of the misty night,	
And Titan playing on the eastern streams,	
clear the dewy air with springing light,	
Sir Guyon mindful of his vow plight°,	*pledged*
Up rose from drowsy couch, and him addressed	
Unto the journey which he had behight°:	*vowed*
His puissant° arms about his noble breast,	*mighty*
And many-folded shield he bound about his wrest°.	*wrist*

2

Then taking congé[1] of that virgin pure,	
The bloody-handed babe unto her truth	
Did earnestly commit, and her conjure°,	*promise*
In virtuous lore to train his tender youth,	
And all that gentle nuriture° ensueth°:	*nurture / take place*
And that so soon as riper years he raught°,[2]	*reached*

1. This was a formal taking of leave, perhaps including a bow and the exchange of email addresses.
2. I.e., when he was older.

He might for memory of that day's ruth°,   *sorrow*
Be called Ruddymane, and thereby taught,
To avenge his parents' death on them, that had it wrought.[3]

3

So forth he fared, as now befell, on foot,
Since his good steed is lately from him gone;
Patience perforce°; helpless what may it boot°   *required / gain*
To fret for anger, or for grief to moan?
His Palmer now shall foot no more alone:
So fortune wrought, as under green woods side
He lately heard that dying lady groan,
He left his steed without, and spear beside,
And rushed in on foot to aid her, ere she died.

4

The whiles a losel° wandering by the way,   *worthless man*
One that to bounty never cast his mind,
Nor thought of honor ever did assay
His baser breast, but in his kestrel[4] kind
A pleasing vein of glory vain did find,[5]
To which his flowing tongue, and troublous sprite°   *spirit*
Gave him great aid, and made him more inclined:
He that brave steed there finding ready dight°,   *dressed*
Purloined° both steed and spear, and ran away full light.[6]   *stole*

5

Now 'gan his heart all swell in jollity,
And of himself great hope and help conceived,
That puffed up with smoke of vanity,
And with self-lovéd personage deceived,
He 'gan to hope, of men to be received

---

3. Ruddymane, the "bloody-handed babe," is left in the care of Medina to learn to deal "vengeance" on the witch who destroyed his family. Spenser means that the very act of learning temperance is vengeance being worked on intemperance. Ruddymane's name literally means "red-handed."

4. Meet Braggadochio. "Kestrel" is a bird reference meaning he's from the falcon family: proud and haughty, but also a hunter for prey.

5. I.e., honor never passed through this guy's breast; through his heart ran a vein of vain glory. Vain glory is a false joy in worthless accomplishments: a toothy grin on a hill of beans.

6. Braggadochio is the culprit. He purloined Guyon's horse and goods.

For such, as he him thought, or feign would be:
But for in court gay portance° he perceived,   *purpose*
And gallant show to be in greatest gree°,   *favor*
Eftsoones° to court he cast to advance his first degree.   *soon*

6

And by the way he chanced to espy
One sitting idle on a sunny bank,
To whom vaunting in great bravery,
As peacock,[7] that his painted plumes doth prance,
He smote his courser in the trembling flank,
And to him threatened his heart-thrilling spear:
The silly man seeing him ride so rank,
And aim at him, fell flat to ground for fear,
And crying mercy loud, his piteous hands 'gan rear.[8]

7

Thereat the scarecrow[9] waxed wondrous proud,
Through fortune of his first adventure fair,
And with big thundering voice reviled him loud;
"Vile caitiff°, vassal of dread and despair,   *coward*
Unworthy of the common breathèd air,
Why livest thou, dead dog, a longer day,
And doest not unto death thyself prepare.
Die, or thyself my captive yield for aye°;   *ever*
Great favor I thee grant, for answer thus to stay."

8

"Hold, O dear Lord, hold your dead-doing hand,"
Then loud he cried, "I am your humble thrall."
"Ah wretch," quoth he, "thy destinies withstand
My wrathful will, and do for mercy call.
I give thee life: therefore prostrated fall,

7. So basically we have a couple of birdish fellows: One is haughty and proud; the other is what we might call in the vernacular a wimp. And from these two fellows comes the beloved insult "bird brain."

8. Braggadochio, feeling full of beans, is on the way to court, when he meets Trompart. Braggadochio waves his (Guyon's) spear around wildly, threatening the feeble Trompart.

9. The scarecrow is Braggadochio, and the fact that he's called a scarecrow is mildly amusing as it is unclear whether he merely scares other "birds" or if he might also scare himself.

And kiss my stirrup; that thy homage be."[10]
The miser threw himself, as an offal°,   *butchered waste*
Straight at his foot in base humility,
And cleped° him his liege, to hold of him in fee.   *called*

9

So happy peace they made and fair accord:
Eftsoones° this liege-man 'gan to wax more bold,   *soon after*
And when he felt the folly of his lord,
In his own kind he 'gan him self unfold:
For he was wily witted, and grown old
In cunning slights and practic knavery°.   *deceitful dealings*
From that day forth he cast for to uphold
His idle humor with fine flattery,
And blow the bellows to his swelling vanity.[11]

10

Trompart fit man for Braggadochio,
To serve at court in view of vaunting eye;
Vain-glorious man, when fluttering wind does blow
In his light wings, is lifted up to sky:[12]
The scorn of knighthood and true chivalry,
To think without dessert of gentle deed,
And noble worth to be advancéd high:
Such praise is shame; but honor virtue's meed°   *reward*
Doth bear the fairest flower in honorable seed.

11

So forth they pass, a well consorted pair,
Till that at length with Archimage they meet:
Who seeing one that shone in armor fair,
On goodly courser° thundering with his feet,   *battle horse*
Eftsoones° supposed him a person meet,   *soon*
Of his revenge to make the instrument:

10. Oh yeah. He's really milking this: "And while yer at it, could you give me a back rub? How about a foot massage?"

11. After some time, Trompart catches on to the fact that Braggadochio is a bit on the dim side, but he's cunning and continues to play along, flattering Braggadochio and laughing at his lame jokes.

12. Spenser is saying that Trompart is a fit companion for Braggadochio. Braggadochio is a braggart and Trompart is a flatterer. Trompart is the "light wind that lifts Braggadochio's wings to the sky."

For since the Redcross knight he earst° did weet°,   *formerly / know*
To been with Guyon knit in one consent,
The ill, which earst° to him, he now to Guyon meant.[13]   *formerly*

12

And coming close to Trompart 'gan inquire
Of him, what mighty warrior that might be,
That rode in golden sell° with single spear,   *saddle*
But wanted sword to wreak his enmity.[14]
"He is a great adventurer," said he,
"That hath his sword through hard assay° forgone,   *trial*
And now hath vowed, till he avenged be,
Of that despight°, never to wearen° none;   *insult / wear*
That spear is him enough to done a thousand groan."[15]

13

The enchanter greatly joyed in the vaunt,
And weened° well ere° long his will to win,   *thought / before*
And both his foe with equal foil to daunt.[16]
Though to him louting° lowly, did begin   *bowing*
To plain° of wrongs, which had committed been   *complain*
By Guyon, and by that false Redcross knight,
Which two through treason and deceitful gin°,   *plot*
Had slain Sir Mordant, and his lady bright:
That mote° him honor win, to wreak so foul despight.[17]   *might*

14

Therewith all suddenly he seemed enraged,[18]
And threatened death with dreadful countenance,
As if their lives had in his hand been gauged;

13. As our two friends continue on, they run into our old enemy Archimago. Archimago sees a knight and that's all he needs. Formerly, Redcross was his rival, now Guyon makes the list because he knows they are friends. He may even think that Braggadochio is Guyon at first. Remember he has his horse and some armor.

14. Archimago is asking Trompart who Braggadochio is and why he hasn't got a sword.

15. I.e., "Well, my master is so brave he has vowed to only use a spear to fight his enemies, and well, he's done great damage to thousands."

16. Archimago is excited because he thinks he's found a knight who's strong enough to take both Redcross and Guyon. Yeah right.

17. So in order to get things riled up, Archimago tells Braggadochio that Guyon and Redcross killed Sir Mordant and Amavia.

18. Braggadochio is getting miffed.

And with stiff force shaking his mortal lance,
To let him weet° his doughty valiance,[19]   *know*
Thus said; "Old man, great sure shall be thy meed°,   *reward*
If where those knights for fear of due vengeance
Do lurk, thou certainly to me areed°,   *tell*
That I may wreak on them their heinous hateful deed."

15

"Certes°, my lord," said he, "that shall I soon,   *certainly*
And give you eke° good help to their decay,   *also*
But mote° I wisely you advise to doon°;   *might / do*
Give no odds to your foes, but do purvey°   *provide*
Yourself of sword before that bloody day:
For they be two the prowest knights on ground,
And oft approved in many hard assay,
And eke° of surest steel, that may be found,   *also*
Do arm yourself against that day, them to confound."

16

"Dotard,"[20] said he, "let be thy deep advise;
Seems that through many years thy wits thee fail,
And that weak eld° hath left thee nothing wise,   *old age*
Else never should thy judgment be so frail,
To measure manhood by the sword or mail.
Is not enough four quarters of a man,
Withouten sword or shield, an host to quail°?   *waver*
Thou little wotest°, what this right hand can: *know*
Speak they, which have beheld the battles, which it won."[21]

17

The man was much abashed at his boast;
Yet well he wist°, that who so would contend   *knew*
With either of those knights on even coast,
Should need of all his arms, him to defend;
Yet feared least his boldness should offend,

19. Basically Braggadochio is waving his spear around all macho in order to show Archimago how buff and brave he is.

20. A dotard is one who is senile, usually old, and losing mental faculties. Have fun with that one.

21. When Archimago suggested that Braggadochio get a sword, Braggadochio says that arms and legs are all the sword he needs and everyone who's ever seen him fight knows that.

When Braggadochio said, "Once I did swear,
When with one sword seven knights I brought to end,
Thence forth in battle never sword to bear,
But it were that, which noblest knight on earth doth wear."[22]

18

"Perdie[23] sir knight," said then the enchanter[24] blue,
"That shall I shortly purchase to your hand:
For now the best and noblest knight alive
Prince Arthur is, that wones° in Faerie Land;   *lives*
He hath a sword, that flames like burning brand.
The same by my device I undertake
Shall by tomorrow by thy side be found."
At which bold word that boaster 'gan to quake,
And wondered in his mind, what mote° that monster make.   *might*

19

He stayed not for more bidding, but away
Was sudden vanished out of his sight:
The northern wind his wings did broad display
At his command, and reared him up light
From off the earth to take his airy flight.
They looked about, but no where could espy
Tract of his foot: then dead through great affright
They both nigh were, and each bade other fly:
Both fled at once, nor ever back returnéd eye.[25]

20

Till that they come unto a forest green,
In which they shroud themselves from causeless fear;
Yet fear them follows still, where so they been,
Each trembling leaf, and whistling wind they hear,
As ghastly bug their hair on end does rear:[26]
Yet both do strive their fearfulness to feign.

22. Braggadochio says that he once swore that he would never use a sword unless it was the sword of the noblest knight on earth.

23. A common oath, meaning "by God."

24. The "enchanter" is Archimago of course.

25. Archimago disappears, and Braggadochio and Trompart run away crying for their mommies.

26. Braggadochio and Trompart are hiding in the woods, and every little sound makes them shake and stands their hair on end.

At last they heard a horn that shrilléd clear
Throughout the wood, that echoéd again,
And made the forest ring, as it would rive° in twain.   *split*

21

Eft° through the thick they heard one rudely rush;   *soon*
With noise whereof he from his lofty steed
Down fell to ground, and crept into a bush,[27]
To hide his coward head from dying dread.[28]
But Trompart stoutly stayed to taken heed,
Of what might hap. Eftsoone° there steppéd forth   *soon after*
A goodly lady clad in hunter's weed,[29]
That seemed to be a woman of great worth,
And by her stately portance, born of heavenly birth.[30]

22

Her face so fair as flesh it seeméd not,
But heavenly portrait of bright angel's hue,
Clear as the sky, without blame or blot,
Through goodly mixture of complexions due;
And in her cheeks the vermeil° red did show   *bright red*
Like roses in a bed of lilies shed,
The which ambrosial° odors from them threw,   *sweet*
And gazer's sense with double pleasure fed,
Able to heal the sick, and to revive the dead.

23

In her fair eyes two living lamps did flame,
Kindled above at the heavenly maker's light,
And darted fiery beams out of the same,
So passing persant°, and so wondrous bright,   *piercing*
That quite bereaved the rash beholder's sight:
In them the blinded god° his lustful fire   *Cupid*
To kindle oft assayed°, but had no might;   *tried*
For with dread majesty, and awful ire°,   *wrath*
She broke his wanton darts, and quenchéd base desire.

27. Braggadochio, upon hearing the sound of someone crashing through the woods, jumps off his horse and dives into a nearby bush.

28. That's our brave Braggadochio.

29. That's Belphoebe; she's wearing hunter clothes, probably woodland fatigues.

30. Belphoebe seems to be born of heaven. The following stanzas will prove her perfections.

24

Her ivory forehead, full of bounty brave,
Like a broad table did itself dispread°,   *extend*
For love his lofty triumphs to engrave,
And write the battles of his great godhead:
All good and honor might therein be read:
For there their dwelling was. And when she spake,
Sweet words, like dropping honey she did shed,
And twixt the pearls and rubins° softly brake   *rubies*
A silver sound, that heavenly music seemed to make.

25

Upon her eyelids many graces sate°,   *rested*
Under the shadow of her even brows,
Working belgards° and amorous retrate°,   *beauties / expression*
And everyone her with a grace endows:
And everyone with meekness to her bows.
So glorious mirror of celestial grace,
And sovereign monument of mortal vows,
How shall frail pen describe her heavenly face,
For fear through want of skill her beauty to disgrace?

26

So fair and thousand thousand times more fair
She seemed, when she presented was to sight,
And was clad, for heat of scorching air,
All in a silken camus lily white,
Purfled° upon with many a folded plight,   *decked*
Which all above besprinkled was throughout,
With golden aigulets° that glistered bright,   *ornamental chords*
Like twinkling stars, and all the skirt about
Was hemmed with golden fringe.

27

Below her ham° her weed° were somewhat train,[31]   *thigh / clothes*
And her straight legs most bravely were embailed°   *enclosed*

31. The "train" is the part of a gown the follows behind. One dictionary says that this can sometimes refer to the tail feathers of a bird. This is interesting simply for the fact that Braggadochio and Trompart have both already been described as having various bird-like qualities. Spenser is contrasting Belphoebe with Braggadochio and Trompart, specifically Braggadochio. Keep your eye out for more connections.

In gilden buskins° of costly cordwain,[32]   *half boots*
All barred with golden bands, which were entailed°   *engraved*
With curious antics and full fair amailed°:   *decorated*
Before they fastened were under her knee
In a rich jewel, and therein entrailed°   *wrapped*
The ends of all their knots, that none might see,
How they within their foldings close enwrappéd be.

28

Like two fair marble pillars they were seen,
Which do the temple of the gods support,
Whom all the people deck with garlands green,
And honor in their festival resort;
Those same with stately grace, and princely port
She taught to tread, when she herself would grace,
But with the woody nymphs when she did play,
Or when the flying libbardé° she did chase,   *leopard*
She could them nimbly move, and after fly apace.[33]

29

And in her hand a sharp bore-spear she held,
And at her back a bow and quiver gay,
Stuffed with steel-headed darts, wherewith she quelled
The savage beasts in her victorious play,
Knit with a golden baldric°, which forelay   *belt*
Athwart° her snowy breast, and did divide   *across*
Her dainty paps°; which like young fruit in May   *breasts*
Now little 'gan to swell, and being tied,
Through her thin weed° their places only signified.   *clothes*

30

Her yellow locks crisped, like golden wire,
About her shoulders were loosely shed,
And when the wind amongst them did inspire,
They waved like a pennon° wide dispread°,   *banner / unfurled*
And low behind her back were scattered:
And whether art it were, or heedless hap,
As through the flowering forest rash she fled,
In her rude hairs sweet flowers themselves did lap,
And flourishing fresh leaves and blossoms did enwrap.[34]

32. That's cordovan, which is a fine leather.
33. That is to say, she could keep up with a leopard on foot.
34. That, my friends, is Spenser's version of Proverbs 31. What a woman!

31

Such as Diana by the sandy shore
Of swift Eurotas, or on Cynthus green,
Where all the Nymphs have her unwares° forlore°,   *unaware / forsaken*
Wandereth alone with bow and arrows keen,
To seek her game:[35] Or as that famous queen
Of Amazons, whom Pyrrhus did destroy,
The day that first of Priam she was seen,
Did show herself in great triumphant joy,
To succor the weak state of sad afflicted Troy.[36]

32

Such when as heartless Trompart her did view,
He was dismayed in his coward mind,
And doubted, whether he himself should show,
Or fly away, or bide alone behind:
Both fear and hope he in her face did find,
When she at last him spying thus bespake;
"Hail groom; didst not thou see a bleeding hind,
Whose right haunch earst my steadfast arrow strake°?   *strike*
If thou didst, tell me, that I may her overtake."[37]

33

Wherewith revived, this answer forth he threw;
"O goddess, for such I thee take to be
For neither doth thy face terrestrial show,
Nor voice sound mortal; I avow to thee,
Such wounded beast, as that, I did not see,
Since earst° into this forest wild I came.   *earlier*
But mote° thy goodly head forgive it me,   *might*
To weet°, which of the gods I shall thee name,   *know*
That unto thee due worship I may rightly frame."[38]

35. "Such as Diana . . ." Robert Kellog says that this is an illusion to the *Aeneid*, a description of Dido, a great and beautiful queen, though she took her own life.

36. Kellog also connects this to Penthesileia, another beautiful and courageous woman. Compare this with Braggadochio, who's still hiding in the bushes.

37. Belphoebe is looking for a deer she just shot with her bow. Notice how we have seen that both Belphoebe and Braggadochio can run. But Belphoebe runs towards a challenge, and Braggadochio runs away. Another similarity and contrast is the fact that they are both hunters (remember Braggadochio was described as 'kestrel' earlier) but in entirely different ways.

38. Three out of four literary critics agree: Trompart is a dork.

34

To whom she thus; but ere her words ensued,
Unto the bush her eye did sudden glance,
In which vain Braggadochio was moved,
And saw it stir: she left her piercing lance,
And towards 'gan a deadly shaft advance,
In mind to mark the beast.[39] At which sad stower°,[40]   *peril*
Trompart forth stepped, to stay the mortal chance,
Out crying, "O whatever heavenly power,
Or earthly wight° thou be, withhold this deadly hour.   *creature*

35

"O stay thy hand, for yonder is no game
For thy fierce arrows, them to exercise,
But lo my lord, my liege, whose warlike name,
Is far renowned through many bold emprise°;   *achievements*
And now in shade he shrouded yonder lies."[41]
She staid: with that he crawled out of his nest,[42]
Forth creeping on his caitiff° hands and thighs,   *coward*
And standing stoutly up, his lofty crest
Did fiercely shake, and rouse, as coming late from rest.

36

As fearful fowl, that long in secret cave
For dread of soaring hawk herself hath hid,
Not caring how, her silly life to save,
She her gay painted plumes disordered,
Seeing at last herself from danger rid,
Peeps forth, and soon renews her native pride;
She 'gins her feathers foul disfigured
Proudly to prune°, and set on every side,   *preen*
So shakes off shame, nor thinks how erst° she did her hide.[43]   *earlier*

39. Uh-oh, Braggadochio's in for it now.
40. That's the bush where Braggadochio is roosting.
41. I.e. "That's no deer, ma'am, that's my brave master." Sheesh.
42. Ha! He's a bird alright, nesting for fear. Watch the bird imagery continue in the following lines.
43. Just picture Braggadochio like this bird. Braggadochio hides in the bushes until he realizes that Belphoebe has seen him.

37

So when her goodly visage° he beheld,   *face*
He 'gan himself to vaunt: but when he viewed
Those deadly tools, which in her hand she held,
Soon into other fits he was transmewed,[44]
Till she to him her gracious speech renewed;
"All hail, sir knight, and well may thee befall,
As all the like, which honor have pursued
Through deeds of arms and prowess martial;
All virtue merits praise, but such the most of all."

38

To whom he thus: "O fairest under sky,
True be thy words, and worthy of thy praise,
That warlike feats doest highest glorify.
Therein have I spent all my youthly days,
And many battles fought, and many frays
Throughout the world, where so they might be found,
Endeavoring my dreaded name to raise
Above the moon, that fame may it resound
In her eternal tromp, with laurel garland crowned.[45]

39

"But what art thou, O lady, which doest range
In this wild forest, where no pleasure is,
And doest not it for joyous court exchange,
Amongst thine equal peers, where happy bliss
And all delight does reign much more than this?
There thou mayest love, and dearly lovéd be,
And swim in pleasure, which thou here doest miss;
There mayest thou best be seen, and best mayest see:
The wood is fit for beasts, the court is fit for thee."

40

"Who so in pomp of proud estate" quoth she.
"Does swim, and bathes himself in courtly bliss,
Does waste his days in dark obscurity,
And in oblivion ever buried is:
Where ease abounds, it's eath° to do amiss;   *easy*

44. "Changed," or when two cats trade voice boxes.
45. Braggadochio is living up to his name well, don't you think?

But who his limbs with labors, and his mind
Behaves with cares, cannot so easy miss.
Abroad in arms, at home in studious kind
Who seeks with painful toil, shall honor soonest find.[46]

41

"In woods, in waves, in wars she wants to dwell,
And will be found with peril and with pain;
Nor can the man, that molds in idle cell,
Unto her happy mansion attain:
Before her gate high God did sweat ordain,
And wakeful watches ever to abide:
But easy is the way, and passage plain
To pleasure's palace; it may soon be spied,
And day and night her doors to all stand open wide.[47]

42

"In prince's court—" The rest she would have said,
But that the foolish man, filled with delight
Of her sweet words, that all his sense dismayed,
And with her wondrous beauty ravished quite,
'Gan burn in filthy lust, and leaping light,
Thought in his bastard arms her to embrace.
With that she swerving back, her javelin bright
Against him bent, and fiercely did menace:
So turned her about, and fled away apace.°[48]   *quickly*

43

Which when the peasant saw, amazed he stood,
And grieved at her flight; yet durst° he not   *dared*
Pursue her steps, through wild unknown wood;
Besides he feared her wrath, and threatened shot
Whiles in the bush he lay, not yet forgot:
Nor cared he greatly for her presence vain,
But turning said to Trompart, "What foul blot

---

46. Braggadochio asks Belphoebe why she isn't at the court, and she explains to him that honor is best sought actively and with hard work. This is another contrast to Braggadochio. He is on his way to court. Belphoebe is busying herself with work away from court.

47. The "she" in this stanza is honor. Sweat and hard work is the way to honor, but ease will lead to wrongdoing.

48. Girls, take note. The moral of the story: Keep a javelin in your purse and don't be afraid to use it.

Is this to knight, that lady should again
Depart to woods untouched, and leave so proud disdain?"

44

"Perdie°," said Trompart, "let her pass at will,   *truly*
Least by her presence danger might befall.
For who can tell and sure I fear it ill
But that she is some power celestial?
For whiles she spake, her great words did appall
My feeble courage, and my heart oppress,
That yet I quake and tremble over all."
"And I," said Braggadocio, "thought no less,
When first I heard her horn sound with such ghastliness.

45

"For from my mothers womb this grace I have
Me given by eternal destiny,
That earthly thing may not my courage brave
Dismay with fear, or cause one foot to fly,
But either hellish fiends, or powers on high:
Which was the cause, when earst° that horn I heard,   *earlier*
Weening° it had been thunder in the sky,   *thinking*
I hid myself from it, as one afeared;
But when I other knew, myself I boldly reared.[49]

46

"But now for fear of worse, that may betide,
Let us soon hence depart." They soon agree;
So to his steed he got, and 'gan to ride,
As one unfit therefore, that all might see
He had not trainéd been in chivalry.
Which well that valiant courser[50] did discern;
For he despised to tread in due degree,
But chafed and foamed, with courage fierce and stern,
And to be eased of that base burden still did earn.[51]

49. Trompart tells Braggadochio it's probably best that Belphoebe got away because she appeared to be a goddess. Braggadochio agrees and assures Trompart that this is why he hid in the first place, but when he thought better of it, he came out to investigate. What a fool.

50. A "courser" can refer to either a horse or a hunter. Thus Spenser is playing with this ambiguity here. Belphoebe discerned Braggadochio's lack of chivalry as did his horse because he could not ride well.

51. The only thing Braggadochio works hard at is ridding himself of chivalry.

 Riddle Me This

Directions: Identify where in the story the following quotes came from. Explain what they mean and their significance to the story.

1. "Once I did swear,
   When with one sword seven knights I brought to end,
   Thence forth in battle never sword to bear,
   But it were that, which noblest knight on earth doth wear."

2. "But mote thy goodly head forgive it me,
   To weet, which of the gods I shall thee name,
   That unto thee due worship I may rightly frame."

3. "The wood is fit for beasts, the court is fit for thee."

Canto IV.

Guyon does Furor bind in chains,
and stops Occasion:
Delivers Phedon, and therefore
by Strife is railed upon.

1

In brave pursuit of honorable deed,
There is I know not what great difference
Between the vulgar and the noble seed,
Which unto things of valorous pretence
Seems to be born by native influence;
As feats of arms, and love to entertain,
But chiefly skill to ride, seems a science
Proper to gentle blood; some others feign
To manage steeds, as did this vaunter°; but in vain.[1]   *braggart*

2

But he the rightful owner of that steed,
Who well could manage and subdue his pride,
The whiles on foot was forced for to yeed°,   *go*
With that black Palmer, his most trusty guide;
Who suffered not his wandering feet to slide.[2]

---

1. The "vaunter" who attempted to manage a steed was, of course, Braggadochio.
2. Notice that Spenser connects the nobility of being able to ride a horse with humility. Humility is the ability to manage and subdue pride. Guyon can do it; Braggadochio cannot.

But when strong passion, or weak fleshliness
Would from the right way seek to draw him wide,
He would through temperance and steadfastness,
Teach him the weak to strengthen and the strong suppress.[3]

3

It fortuned forth faring on his way,
He saw from far, or seemed for to see
Some troublous uproar or contentious fray°,   *struggle*
Whereto he drew in haste it to agree.
A madman, or that feignéd mad to be,
Drew by the hair along upon the ground,
A handsome stripling° with great cruelty,   *young man*
Whom sore he beat, and gored with many a wound,
That cheeks with tears, and sides with blood did all abound.[4]

4

And him behind, a wicked hag° did stalk,   *beastly woman*
In ragged robes, and filthy disarray,
Her other leg was lame, that she no't° walk,   *couldn't*
But on a staff her feeble steps did stay;
Her locks, that loathly were and hoary gray,
Grew all afore°, and loosely hung unrolled,   *on the front*
But all behind was bald, and worn away,
That none thereof could ever taken hold,
And eke° her face ill favored, full of wrinkles old.   *also*

5

And ever as she went, her tongue did walk
In foul reproach, and terms of vile despite,
Provoking him by her outrageous talk,
To heap more vengeance on that wretched wight°;[5]   *creature*
Sometimes she raught° him stones, where with to smite,   *gave*
Sometimes her staff, though it her one leg were,
Withouten which she could not go upright;

3. Here Spenser continues to elaborate on the nature of temperance. It is the ability
to strengthen the weaknesses of our bodies and to weaken those unruly passions that
have become strong.
4. As Guyon and the Palmer are traveling along they come upon a young man being
dragged by the hair and beaten by a madman.
5. "Wight" refers to the young man.

Nor any evil means she did forbear,
That might him move to wrath, and indignation rear.[6]

6

The noble Guyon moved with great remorse,
Approaching, first the hag did thrust away,
And after adding more impetuous force,
His mighty hands did on the madman lay,
And plucked him back; who all on fire straightway,
Against him turning all his fell intent,
With beastly brutish rage 'gan him assay°,   *attack*
And smote, and bit, and kicked, and scratched, and rent,
And did he wist° not what in his avengement.[7]   *know*

7

And sure he was a man of mickle° might,   *great*
Had he had governance, it well to guide:
But when the frantic fit inflamed his sprite°,   *spirit*
His force was vain, and stroke more often wide,
Than at the aimed mark, which he had eyed:
And oft himself he chanced to hurt unwares,
Whilst reason blent° through passion, nought descried,[8]   *blinded*
But as a blindfold bull at random fares,
And where he hits, nought knows and whom he hurts, nought cares.[9]

8

His rude assault and rugged handling
Strange seemed to the knight, that aye° with foe   *ever*
In fair defense and goodly managing
Of arms was want to fight, yet nathemoe°   *nevertheless*
Was he abashed now not fighting so,
But more enfierced through his currish° play,   *cowardly*
Him sternly gripped, and hauling to and fro,

6. This old hag limps behind "walking her tongue", heaping up insults, and taunting the man to beat the fellow harder. There's nothing like team work!

7. Guyon knocks the old hag out of the way and then pulls the madman off the man he was beating. Immediately the madman turns on Guyon and began swinging wildly, kicking, biting, and scratching. He's so mad that he doesn't even know what he's doing.

8. "Nought descried" means that he saw nothing.

9. Notice the destructive nature of fury. It makes a man blind. He doesn't even notice who he's hurting or that he's usually hurting himself.

To overthrow him strongly did assay,
But overthrew himself unwares, and lower lay.[10]

9

And being down the villain sore did beat,
And bruise with clownish fists his manly face:
And eke° the hag with many a bitter threat,   *also*
Still called upon to kill him in the place.[11]
With whose reproach and odious menace
The knight emboiling° in his haughty heart,   *burning*
Knit all his forces, and 'gan soon unbrace°   *loosen*
His grasping hold: so lightly did upstart,
And drew his deadly weapon, to maintain his part.

10

Which when the Palmer saw, he loudly cried,
"Not so, O Guyon, never think that so
That monster can be mastered or destroyed:
He is not, ah, he is not such a foe,
As steel can wound, or strength can overthrow.
That same is Furor, curséd cruél wight°,   *creature*
That unto knighthood works much shame and woe;
And that same hag, his agéd mother, hight°   *called*
Occasion, the root of all wrath and despite.[12]

11

"With her, who so will raging Furor tame,
Must first begin, and well her amenage°:   *training*
First her restrain from her reproachful blame,
And evil means, with which she doth enrage
Her frantic son, and kindles his courage,
Then when she is withdrawen, or strong withstood,
It's eath° his idle fury to assuage°,   *easy / soothe*
And calm the tempest of his passion wood°;   *mad*
The banks are overflowen, when stoppéd is the flood."[13]

10. He knocked himself down.
11. The hag is taunting Guyon to kill the madman.
12. Spenser finally gives us names to go with these memorable characters. The madman is Furor and the old, taunting hag is his mother, Occasion. The Palmer stops Guyon from attempting to slay Furor because he is not an enemy that is slain in this fashion. Unbridled anger does not subdue anger.
13. The way to deal with Furor is to deal with his mother first. As soon as she is taken care of, Furor will take care of himself.

12

Therewith Sir Guyon left his first emprise°,   *mission*
And turning to that woman, fast her hent°   *seized*
By the hoary locks, that hung before her eyes,
And to the ground her threw: yet n'ould° she stent°[14]   *nor would / restrain*
Her bitter railing and foul revilement,
But still provoked her son to wreak° her wrong;   *avenge*
But natheless° he did her still torment,   *nevertheless*
And catching hold of her ungracious tongue,
Thereon an iron lock did fasten firm and strong.[15]

13

Then when as use of speech was from her reft°,   *taken*
With her two crooked hands she signs did make,
And beckoned him, the last help she had left:
But he that last left help away did take,
And both her hands fast bound unto a stake,
That she not stir. Then 'gan her son to fly
Full fast away, and did her quite forsake;
But Guyon after him in haste did hie°,   *go*
And soon him overtook in sad perplexity.

14

In his strong arms he stiffly him° embraced,   *Furor*
Who him gain striving, nought at all prevailed:
For all his power was utterly defaced,
And furious fits at earst° quite weren quailed°:   *first / were overpowered*
Oft he reinforced, and oft his forces failed,
Yet yield he would not, nor his rancor slack.
Then him to ground he cast, and rudely hailed,
And both his hands fast bound behind his back,
And both his feet in fetters to an iron rack.

15

With hundred iron chains he did him bind,
And hundred knots that did him sore constrain:
Yet his great iron teeth he still did grind,
And grimly gnash, threatening revenge in vain:

14. I.e., yet she wouldn't stop.

15. Guyon can't attack Furor with his sword. Rather, he must go to the source and deal with "her" with no gentleness or compassion. Righteous anger is the solution to fury only when it deals with the problem at its root. Occasion must be thrown down and have her tongue silenced with a lock.

His burning eyen°, whom bloody streaks did stain,   *eyes*
Stared full wide, and threw forth sparks of fire,
And more for rank despite, than for great pain,
Shaked his long locks, colored like copper-wire,
And bit his tawny beard to show his raging ire°.[16]   *wrath*

16

Thus when as Guyon Furor had captivéd,
Turning about he saw that wretched squire,
Whom that madman of life nigh late deprived,
Lying on ground, all soiled with blood and mire:
Whom when as he perceived to respire°,[17]   *breathe*
He 'gan to comfort, and his wounds to dress.
Being at last recured°, he 'gan inquire,   *recovered*
What hard mishap him brought to such distress,[18]
And made that caitiff's° thrall°, the thrall of wretchedness.   *wretch's / bondage*

17

With heart then throbbing, and with watery eyes,
"Fair sir," quoth he, "what man can shun the hap,
That hidden lies unwares him to surprise?
Misfortune waits advantage to entrap
The man most wary in her whelming lap.
So me weak wretch, of many weakest one,
Unweeting° and unware of such mishap,   *unthinking*
She brought to mischief through Occasion,
Where this same wicked villain did me light upon.

18

"It was a faithless squire, that was the source
Of all my sorrow, and of these sad tears,
With whom from tender dug° of common nurse,   *breast*
At once I was up brought, and eft° when years   *afterward*
More ripe us reason lent to choose our peers,
Ourselves in league of vowed love we knit:

16. Easy, boy. All Fury needs is a choke chain, a muzzle, a few tattoos, and a few pieces of metal in his face and he'd be the lead singer of some "Christian" rock band.

17. He was still breathing.

18. After Guyon took care of Furor and his ugly mother, he dressed the squire's wounds. When he seemed to be feeling better, Guyon asked him what happened and how he got into this mess.

Guyon

The name Guyon means something like "lively struggle." If Sir Guyon is the Knight of Temperance as Spenser says he is, how is temperance exemplified through a "lively struggle"? First, temperance, according to this book of the *Faerie Queene*, is right action and reaction in every situation. It is important to point out that temperance is right *action*. Temperance is not merely a right way of thinking or viewing the world. Temperance has hands with which to swing a sword, a mouth with which to speak the truth, and legs with which to flee evil and temptation. Second, temperance is a struggle, a wrestling match. It takes wisdom and discernment to know when to stand, fight, and utterly destroy, and when to run like the dickens. It must know when to argue and seek to persuade, and when to shut up and let silence answer foolishness. Temperance must sometimes walk a tightrope between extremes and at other times it must veer headlong into justice and peace. Finally, temperance is *lively*. Whether it be emotion or action, thoughts or words, the temperate man is full of life and vigor. He pours himself into every situation with energy and imagination. There is no room for half-heartedness. Temperance demands exuberant, faithful living.

In which we long time without jealous fears,
Or faulty thoughts continued, as was fit;
And for my part I vow, dissembled not a whit°.[19]   *bit*

19

"It was my fortune common to that age,
To love a lady fair of great degree,
The which was born of noble parentage,
And set in highest seat of dignity,
Yet seemed no less to love, than loved to be:[20]
Long I her served, and found her faithful still,

19. The youth is telling the story of all his sorrow. It all began, he says, with a beautiful friendship between him and another squire. They had the same nurse, they were best friends, they played on the same baseball teams growing up, and he was always faithful.

20. You know . . . they were in love.

Nor ever thing could cause us disagree:
Love that two hearts makes one, makes eke° one will: *also*
Each strove to please, and other's pleasure to fulfill.

20

"My friend, hight° Philemon, I did partake°   *called / tell*
Of all my love and all my privity°;[21]   *secrets*
Who greatly joyous seemed for my sake,
And gracious to that lady, as to me,
Nor ever wight°, that mote° so welcome be,   *creature / might*
As he to her, withouten blot or blame,
Nor ever thing, that she could think or see,
But unto him she would impart the same:
O wretched man, that would abuse so gentle dame.

21

At last such grace I found, and means I wrought,
That I that lady to my spouse had won;
Accord of friends, consent of parents sought,
Affiance made, my happiness begun,
There wanted naught but few rites to be done,
Which marriage make;[22] that day too far did seem:
Most joyous man, on whom the shining sun,
Did show his face, myself I did esteem,
And that my falser friend did no less joyous deem.

22

"But ere° that wishéd day his beam disclosed,   *before*
He either envying my toward good,
Or of himself to treason ill disposed
One day unto me came in friendly mood,
And told for secret how he understood
That lady whom I had to me assigned,
Had both disdained her honorable blood,
And eke° the faith, which she to me did bind;   *also*
And therefore wished me stay, till I more truth should find.[23]

21. He says his best friend's name was Philemon. He told Philemon everything about his love.

22. So he courted this woman, and they became engaged. He was just waiting for the wedding day.

23. One day, when the marriage was drawing near, Philemon came to the squire and told him that he believed his fiancé was being dishonorable and unfaithful to him.

23

"The gnawing anguish and sharp jealousy,
Which his sad speech infixed in my breast,
Rankled so sore, and festered inwardly,
That my engrievéd mind could find no rest,
Till that the truth thereof I did outwrest°,   *find out*
And him besought by that same sacred band
Betwixt us both, to counsel me the best.
He then with solemn oath and plighted hand
Assured ere° long the truth to let me understand.   *before*

24

"Ere° long with like again he boarded° me,   *before / answered*
Saying, he now had bolted° all the flour,   *sifted*
And that it was a groom of base degree,
Which of my love was partner paramour°:   *lover*
Who used in a dark-some inner bower
Her oft to meet: which better to approve,
He promised to bring me at that hour,
When I should see, that would me nearer move,
And drive me to withdraw my blind abuséd love.

25

"This graceless man for furtherance of his guile,
Did court the handmaid of my lady dear,
Who glad to embosom° his affection vile,   *cherish*
Did all she might, more pleasing to appear.[24]
One day to work her to his will more near,
He wooed her thus: "Pryene," so she hight°,   *was called*
"What great despite doth fortune to thee bear,
Thus lowly to abase thy beauty bright,
That it should not deface all other's lesser light?[25]

26

"'But if she[26] had her least help to thee lent,
To adorn thy form according thy desert,

24. The "graceless man" is Philemon. He plotted against our squire. He began seeing the handmaid of the fiancé, and she really liked his attention.
25. I.e., "Pryene, fortune has granted you great beauty. Why do you hide it?" Pryene is the name of the handmaid that Philemon is courting.
26. "She" is fortune.

Their blazing pride thou wouldest soon have blent°,   *spoiled*
And stained their praises with thy least good part;
Nor should fair Claribell with all her art,
Though she thy lady be, approach thee near;
For proof thereof, this evening, as thou art,
Array thyself in her most gorgeous gear,
That I may more delight in thy embracement dear.'[27]

27

"The maiden proud through praise, and mad through love
Him hearkened to, and soon herself arrayed,
The whiles to me the treachor° did remove   *traitor*
His crafty engine°, and as he had said,   *plot*
Me leading, in a secret corner laid,
The sad spectator of my tragedy;
Where left, he went, and his own false part played,
Disguised like that groom of base degree,
Whom he had feigned the abuser of my love to be.[28]

28

"Eftsoones° he came unto the appointed place,   *soon*
And with him brought Pryene, rich arrayed,
In Claribella's clothes. Her proper face
I not discernéd in that dark-some shade,
But weend° it was my love, with whom he played.   *thought*
Ah God, what horror and tormenting grief
My heart, my hands, mine eyes, and all assayed°?   *attacked*
Me liefer° were ten thousand deaths proof,[29]   *willingly*
Than wound of jealous worm, and shame of such reproof.

29

"I home returning, fraught with foul despite°,   *hatred*
And chawing vengeance all the way I went,
Soon as my loathéd love appear in sight,

27. I.e., "If you wore Claribell's clothes tonight, you would be far more beautiful than even she is. And I would love you more." Claribell is the squire's fiancée.
28. So Philemon sets up the scene. He's dressed up like the lover and Pryene is dressed up like Claribell. They're going to play kissy face and our poor squire is going to be hiding in the shadows watching it all unfold. As my wife pointed out, this is kind of like Shakespeare's *Much Ado About Nothing.*
29. I.e., "I would have preferred ten thousand deaths . . ."

With wrathful hand I slew her innocent;
That after soon I dearly did lament:
For when the cause of that outrageous deed
Demanded, I made plain and evident,
Her faulty handmaid, which that bale° did breed,   *sorrow*
Confessed, how Philemon her wrought to change her weed°.[30]   *clothes*

30

"Which when I heard, with horrible affright
And hellish fury all enraged, I sought
Upon myself that vengeable despite
To punish:[31] Yet it better first I thought,
To wreak my wrath on him, that first it wrought.
To Philemon, false faitour° Philemon   *traitor*
I cast to pay, that I so dearly bought;
Of deadly drugs I gave him drink anon°,   *at once*
And washed away his guilt with guilty potion.[32]

31

"Thus heaping crime on crime, and grief on grief,
To loss of love adjoining loss of friend,
I meant to purge both with a third mischief,
And in my woes beginner it to end:
That was Pryene; she did first offend,
She last should smart: with which cruel intent,
When I at her my murderous blade did bend,
She fled away with ghastly dreariment°,   *dreariment*
And I pursuing my fell purpose, after went.[33]

32

"Fear gave her wings, and rage enforced my flight;
Through woods and plains so long I did her chase,
Till this madman, whom your victorious might
Hath now fast bound, me met in middle space,

30. Did you catch all that? The young man thought Claribell was unfaithful, and in his anger killed his fiancé without asking questions. When Pryene found out what happened she confessed the whole thing. It had been her who had been with Philemon. He had asked her to wear Claribell's clothes.
   31. His first impulse is to punish himself.
   32. Philemon got the cup of death. But fury is a fire that grows.
   33. He went after Pryene in order to finish off the last of the "guilty."

As I her, so he me pursued apace°,   *swiftly*
And shortly overtook: I breathing ire°,   *wrath*
Sore chafed at my stay in such a case,
And with my heat kindled his cruel fire;
Which kindled once, his mother did more rage inspire.[34]

33

"Betwixt them both, they have me done° to die,   *marked*
Through wounds and strokes and stubborn handling,
That death were better, than such agony,
As grief and fury unto me did bring;
Of which in me yet sticks the mortal sting,
That during life will never be appeased."
When he thus ended had his sorrowing,
Said Guyon, "Squire, sore have ye been diseased;
But all your hurts may soon through temperance be eased."[35]

34

Then 'gan the Palmer thus, "Most wretched man,
That to affections does the bridle lend;
In their beginning they are weak and wan°,   *pale*
But soon through sufferance grow to fearful end;
Whiles they are weak betimes° with them contend: *quickly*
For when they once to perfect strength do grow,
Strong wars they make, and cruel battery bend
'Gainst fort of reason, it to overthrow:
Wrath, jealousy, grief, love this squire have laid thus low.[36]

35

"Wrath, jealousy, grief, love do thus expel:
Wrath is a fire, and jealousy a weed,
Grief is a flood, and love a monster fell;
The fire of sparks, the weed of little seed,
The flood of drops, the monster filth did breed:
But sparks, seed, drops, and filth do thus delay:
The sparks soon quench, the springing seed outweed°,   *weed out*

34. While he was pursuing Pryene, Furor and Occasion overtook him.

35. I.e., "What you need is a good shot of temperance." Temperance is not only the path of virtuous living. It is also the cure to a life of sorrow.

36. The Palmer is explaining that unbridled affections may not seem too bad when they're little. They may even appear a little cute, but they must be contended with before they grow up to be fierce enemies. This is especially true of boys. A slightly sin-indulged little boy will grow up into a ruinous mess of a man.

The drops dry up, and filth wipe clean away:
So shall wrath, jealousy, grief, love die and decay."[37]

36

"Unlucky Squire" said Guyon "since thou hast
Fallen into mischief through intemperance,
Henceforth take heed of that thou now hast past,
And guide thy ways with wary governance,
Lest worse betide thee by some later chance.
But read° how art thou named, and of what kin°."   *tell / family*
"Phedon I hight°," quoth he, "and do advance   *am named*
Mine ancestry from famous Coradin,
Who first to raise our house to honor did begin."[38]

37

Thus as he spake, lo far away they spied
A varlet° running towards hastily,   *servant*
Whose flying feet so fast their way applied,
That round about a cloud of dust did fly,
Which mingled all with sweat, did dim his eye.
He soon approached, panting, breathless, hot,
And all so soiled, that none could him descry°;   *see*
His countenance was bold, and bashéd° not   *bashful*
For Guyon's looks, but scornful eye-glance at him shot.[39]

38

Behind his back he bore a brazen shield,
On which was drawn fair, in colors fit,
A flaming fire in midst of bloody field,[40]
And round about the wreath this word was writ,
Burnt I do burn. Right well beseemed it,
To be the shield of some redoubted° knight;   *famous*
And in his hand two darts° exceeding flit°,   *daggers / swift*
And deadly sharp he held, whose heads were dight°   *covered*
In poison and in blood of malice and despite.

37. These various manifestations of intemperance are pictured as fire, weeds, a flood, and a monster. Keep these pictures in mind as you read on.

38. At last, a name for our squire! His name is Phedon, descended from Coradin.

39. While Guyon and the Palmer are talking to Phedon, a man comes running down the road at a great speed. He stops, looking at Guyon with scorn.

40. Now after we have just learned from the Palmer, what might you think of this fellow's shield? Who might he be?

39

When he in presence came to Guyon first
He boldly spake, "Sir knight, if knight thou be,
Abandon this forestalled° place at erst°,   *delayed / once*
For fear of further harm, I counsel thee,
Or bide the chance at thine own jeopardy."[41]
The knight at his great boldness wondered,
And though he scorned his idle vanity,
Yet mildly him to purpose answered;
For not to grow of nought he it conjectured.

40

"Varlet°, this place most due to me I deem,   *knight's page*
Yielded by him, that held it forcibly.
But whence should come that harm, which thou doest seem
To threat to him, that minds° his chance to aby°?"   *intends / to take*
"Perdy,°" said he, "here comes and is hard by   *assuredly*
A knight of wondrous power and great assay°,   *adventure*
That never yet encountered enemy,
But did him deadly daunt, or foul dismay;
Nor thou for better hope, if thou his presence stay°."[42]   *await*

41

"How hight he then," said Guyon, "and from whence?"[43]
"Pyrochles is his name, renowned far
For his bold feats and hardy confidence,
Full oft approved in many a cruel war,
The brother of Cymochles, both which are
The sons of old Acrates and Despight,
Acrates son of Phlegeton and Jar;
But Phlegeton is son of Herebus and Night;
But Herebus son of Aeternity is hight°.[44]   *named*

41. The man with the two daggers tells Guyon to leave quickly or else be prepared to face great danger.
42. So the man with the two daggers is a page. He's the footman for a great knight (or so he claims). Guyon says he has the right to remain where he is, but the page says that he'll regret it.
43. I.e., "What's his name and where's he from?" Guyon wants to know who this great knight is.
44. Acrates in Greek means "ungovernable." The other names refer to myths of gods and places of burning, roaring, and chaos. He's got what we might call a "dysfunctional family."

42

"So from immortal race he does proceed,
That mortal hands may not withstand his might,
Drad° for his daring do, and bloody deed;   *dreaded*
For all in blood and spoil is his delight.
His am I Atin,[45] his in wrong and right,
That matter make for him to work upon,
And stir him up to strife and cruel fight.
Fly therefore, fly this fearful stead anon°,   *at once*
Least thy fool-hardice° work thy sad confusion."   *fool-hardiness*

43

"His be that care, whom most it doth concern,"
Said he, "but whither with such hasty flight
Art thou now bound? For well mote° I discern   *might*
Great cause, that carries thee so swift and light."
"My lord," quoth he, "me sent and straight behight°   *promised*
To seek Occasion, where so she be:
For he is all disposed to bloody fight,
And breathes out wrath and heinous cruelty;
Hard is his hap, that first falls in his jeopardy."[46]

44

"Madman," said then the Palmer, "that does seek
Occasion to wrath and cause of strife;
She comes unsought, and shunned follows eke°.   *also*
Happy who can abstain, when rancor rife°   *ripe anger*
Kindles revenge and threats his rusty knife;
Woe never wants, where every cause is caught,
And rash Occasion makes unquiet life."
"Then lo°, where bound she sits, who thou hast sought,"   *look*
Said Guyon, "let that message to thy lord be brought."[47]

45

That when the varlet° heard and saw, straight way   *page*
He waxed wondrous wroth, and said, "Vile knight,
That knights and knighthood doest with shame upbray°,   *rebuke*

45. The page's name is Atin, which means "strife" or "discord."
46. Where is Atin going? His master sent him to get Occasion. Brilliant.
47. The Palmer says that Occasion is only sought by a madman, and Guyon points
her out to Atin. He tells him to tell his lord, Pyrochles.

And showst the example of thy childish might,
With silly weak old woman thus to fight.
Great glory and gay spoil sure hast thou got,
And stoutly proud thy puissance° here in sight;   *might*
That shall Pyrochles well requite°, I wot°,   *repay / know*
And with thy blood abolish so reproachful blot."[48]

46

With that one of his thrillant° darts he threw,   *piercing*
Headed with ire° and vengeable despite;   *wrath*
The quivering steel his aimed end well knew,
And to his breast itself intended right:
But he was wary, and ere it empight°   *plunged*
In the meant mark, advanced his shield atween°,[49]   *between*
On which it seizing, no way enter might,
But back rebounding, left the fork-head keen;
Eftsoones° he fled away, and might no where be seen.   *quickly*

48. Foolish Atin explodes with anger, accusing Guyon and Palmer of beating up on an old, helpless lady. Occasion seems so nice and gentle from a distance.

49. Atin throws one of his daggers at Guyon, but Guyon quickly lifts his shield to guard his chest and deflects the point.

What Do You Know?

Directions: Identify where in the story the following quotes came from. Explain what they mean and their significance to the story.

1. "A madman, or that feignéd mad to be,
   Drew by the hair along upon the ground,
   A handsome stripling with great cruelty,
   Whom sore he beat, and gored with many a wound."

2. "Squire, sore have ye been diseased;
   But all your hurts may soon through temperance be eased."

3. "The fire of sparks, the weed of little seed,
   The flood of drops, the monster filth did breed."

Canto V.

Pyrochles does with Guyon fight,
And Furor's chain unbinds
Of whom sore hurt, for his revenge
Atin Cymochles finds.

1

Whoever doth to temperance apply
His steadfast life, and all his actions frame,
Trust me, shall find no greater enemy,
Than stubborn perturbation°, to the same;   *fury*
To which right well the wise do give that name,
For it the goodly peace of stayed minds
Does overthrow, and troublous war proclaim:
His own woes author, who so bound it finds,
As did Pyrochles,[1] and it willfully unbinds.[2]

2

After that varlet's° flight, it was not long,   *Atin's*
Ere on the plain fast pricking Guyon spied
One in bright arms embattled full strong,

---

1. Pyrochles' name means "moved by fire" or simply "burning." He represents men who are ruled by anger and violence. He is the "great knight" that Atin came announcing to Guyon.

2. This is Spenser's introduction to canto 5. He says that there is no greater enemy in the fight for temperance than fury. And there is no greater woe than for one who finds fury bound and then releases it.

That as the sunny beams do glance and glide
Upon the trembling wave so shinéd bright,
And round about him threw forth sparkling fire,
That seemed him to enflame on every side:
His steed was bloody red, and foaméd ire°,   *wrath*
When with the mastering spur he did him roughly stire°.   *incite*

3

Approaching nigh, he never stayed° to greet,   *waited*
Ne° chaffer° words, proud courage to provoke,   *nor / exchange*
But pricked° so fierce, that underneath his feet   *rode*
The smoldering dust did round about him smoke,
Both horse and man nigh able for to choke;
And fairly couching his steel-headed spear,
Him first saluted with a sturdy stroke;
It booted° naught Sir Guyon coming near   *helped*
To think, such hideous puissance° on foot to bear.[3]   *strength*

4

But lightly shunned it, and passing by,
With his bright blade did smite at him so fell,
That the sharp steel arriving forcibly
On his broad shield, bit not, but glancing fell
On his horse neck before the quilted sell°,   *saddle*
And from the head the body sundered quite.[4]
So him dismounted low, he did compel
On foot with him to match in equal fight;
The truncked° beast fast bleeding, did him foully dight°.   *beheaded / defile*

5

Sore bruised with the fall, he slow up rose,
And all enraged, thus him loudly shent°;   *shouted*
"Disloyal knight, whose coward courage chose
To wreak itself on beast all innocent,
And shunned the mark, at which it should be meant,
Thereby thine arms seem strong, but manhood frail;
So hast thou oft with guile thine honor blent°;   *blended*

3. Pyrochles does not stop to say hello or even ask Guyon to leave. He merely charges full-throttle at Guyon, forcing Guyon to defend himself on foot.
4. Whoops. Guyon swings so hard his sword deflects off of Pyrochles' shield and decapitates the horse he was riding. Yipes.

But little may such guile thee now avail,
If wanted force and fortune do not much me fail."

6

With that he drew his flaming sword, and stroke
At him so fiercely, that the upper marge°   *edge*
Of his seven-folded shield away it took,
And glancing on his helmet, made a large
And open gash therein: were not his targe°,   *shield*
That broke the violence of his intent,
The weary soul from thence it would discharge;
Natheless° so sore a buff to him it lent,   *nevertheless*
That made him reel, and to his breast his beaver° bent.⁵   *helmet*

7

Exceeding wroth was Guyon at that blow,
And much ashamed, that stroke of living arm
Should him dismay, and make him stoop so low,
Though otherwise it did him little harm:⁶
Though hurling high his iron braced arm,
He smote so manly on his shoulder plate,
That all his left side it did quite disarm;
Yet there the steel stayed not, but inly° bate°   *inwardly / bit*
Deep in his flesh, and opened wide a red floodgate.⁷

8

Deadly dismayed, with horror of that dint
Pyrochles was and grievéd eke° entry;   *also*
Yet nathemore° did it his fury stint,   *no more*
But added flame unto his former fire,
That well-nigh molt° his heart in raging ire,   *melted*
Nor thenceforth his approvéd skill, to ward,
Or strike, or hurl, round in warlike gyre°,   *circle*
Remembered he, nor cared for his safeguard,
But rudely raged, and like a cruél tiger fared.⁸

---

5. Pyrochles lets fly his sword and cuts deep into Guyon's shield, even cutting a portion of his helmet.

6. Guyon is not so much hurt as he is embarrassed that Pyrochles took such a nice swipe at him.

7. "What?! It's just a flesh wound!"

8. After Guyon wounds him, Pyrochles no longer fights with the care of a trained knight. He merely swings his sword in anger.

9

He hewed, and lashed, and foined°, and thundered blows,   *thrust*
And every way did seek into his life,
Nor plate, nor mail could ward so mighty throws,
But yielded passage to his cruél knife.
But Guyon, in the heat of all his strife,
Was wary wise, and closely did await
Advantage, whilst his foe did rage most rife;
Sometimes a thwart, sometimes he struck him straight,
And falséd oft his blows, to elude him with such bait.[9]

10

Like as a lion, whose imperial power
A proud rebellious unicorn defies,
To avoid the rash assault and wrathful stour°   *battle*
Of his fierce foe, him to a tree applies,
And when him running in full course he spies,
He slips aside; the whiles that furious beast
His precious horn, sought of his enemies
Strikes in the stock, nor thence can be released,
But to the mighty victor yields a bounteous feast.

11

With such fair slight him Guyon often failed,
Till at the last all breathless, weary, faint
Him spying, with fresh onset he assailed,
And kindling new his courage seeming quaint,
Struck him so hugely, that through great constraint
He made him stoop perforce° unto his knee,   *unavoidably*
And do unwilling worship to the saint,
That on his shield depainted he did see;
Such homage till that instant never learnéd he.[10]

12

Whom Guyon seeing stoop, pursued fast
The present offer of fair victory.
And soon his dreadful blade about he cast,
Wherewith he smote his haughty crest so high,

9. Guyon is using wisdom: dodging, striking, and sometimes faking the force of the blows.

10. Pyrochles finally kneels before Guyon, but only after Guyon has struck him squarely.

That straight on ground made him full low to lie;
Then on his breast his victor foot he thrust:
With that he cried, "Mercy, do me not die,
Nor deem thy force by fortunes doom unjust,
That hath, maugre° her[11] spite, thus low me laid in dust."   *damn*

13

Eftsoones° his cruel hand Sir Guyon stayed°,   *presently / held back*
Tempering the passion with advisement slow,
And mastering might on enemy dismayed:
For the equal die of war he well did know;
Then to him said, "Live and allegiance owe,
To him that gives thee life and liberty,
And henceforth by this day's ensample trow°,   *believe*
That hasty wrath, and heedless hazardry,
Do breed repentance late, and lasting infamy."[12]

14

So up he let him rise, who with grim look
And countenance stern upstanding, 'gan to grind
His grated teeth for great disdain, and shook
His sandy locks, long hanging down behind,
Knotted in blood and dust, for grief of mind,
That he in odds of arms was conquered;
Yet in himself some comfort he did find,
That him so noble knight had mastered,
Whose bounty more than might, yet both he wondered.[13]

15

Which Guyon marking said, "Be not aggrieved,
Sir knight, that thus ye now subdued are:
Was never man, who most conquests achieved
But sometimes had the worse, and lost by war,
Yet shortly gained, that loss exceeded far:
Loss is no shame, nor to be less than foe,
But to be lesser than himself doth mar

11. The "her" is Fortune. Pyrochles is cursing fortune even as he begs for mercy.
12. Guyon agrees to give mercy to Pyrochles on his word that he will not exercise the same foolishness again.
13. Pyrochles' feelings are hurt. There are repressed childhood experiences. There are "inner scars" and lots of other people to blame. And in the end he does what all modern psychobabble teaches. He blames his loss on luck and congratulates himself.

Both losers lot, and victor's praise also.
Vain others overthrows, who self doth overthrow.[14]

16

"Fly, O Pyrochles, fly the dreadful war,
That in thyself thy lesser parts do move,
Outrageous anger, and woe-working jar,
Direful impatience, and heart murdering love;
Those, those thy foes, those warriors far remove,
Which thee to endless bale° captived lead.   *sorrow*
But since in might thou didst my mercy prove,
Of courtesy to me the cause a read°,   *tell me*
That thee against me drew with so impetuous dread."[15]

17

"Dreadless," said he, "that shall I soon declare:
It was complained, that thou hadst done great tort°   *harm*
Unto an agéd woman, poor and bare,
And thralled her in chains with strong effort,
Void of all succor° and needful comfort: *help*
That ill beseems° thee, such as I thee see,   *befits*
To work such shame. Therefore I thee exhort,
To change thy will, and set Occasion free,
And to her captive son yield his first liberty."

18

Thereat Sir Guyon smiled, "And is that all"
Said he, "that thee so sore displeaséd hath?
Great mercy sure, for to enlarge a thrall,
Whose freedom shall thee turn to greatest scath°.[16]   *injury*
Natheless° now quench thy hot emboiling wrath: *nevertheless*
Lo there they be; to thee I yield them free."
Thereat he wondrous glad, out of the path
Did lightly leap, where he them bound did see,
And 'gan to break the bands of their captivity.

14. I.e., it's useless to conquer others, if you are continually conquered by yourself.

15. I.e., "Pyrochles, flee your fury, but since I had mercy on you, why were you so angry to begin with?"

16. Can you hear the sarcasm? "Sure it's a great mercy to free a slave . . . especially the ones that will hurt you."

19

Soon as Occasion felt herself untied,
Before her son could well assoiled° be,   *set free*
She to her use returned, and straight defied
Both Guyon and Pyrochles: "The one," said she
"Because he won; the other because he
Was won": So matter did she make of naught,
To stir up strife, and do them disagree;
But soon as Furor was enlarged°, she sought   *freed*
To kindle his quenchéd fire, and thousand causes wrought.[17]

20

It was not long, ere she inflamed him so,
That he would algates° with Pyrochles fight,   *by all means*
And his redeemer challenged for his foe,
Because he had not well maintained his right,
But yielded had to that same stranger knight:
Now 'gan Pyrochles wax as wood°, as he,   *mad*
And him affronted with impatient might:
So both together fierce engraspéd be,
Whiles Guyon standing by, their uncouth strife does see.[18]

21

Him all that while Occasion did provoke
Against Pyrochles, and new matter framed
Upon the old, him stirring to be wroke°   *avenged*
Of his late wrongs, in which she oft him blamed
For suffering such abuse, as knighthood shamed,
And him disabled quite. But he was wise
Nor would with vain occasions be inflamed;
Yet others she more urgent did devise:
Yet nothing could him to impatience entice.[19]

17. She gives him a thousand reasons to live up to his name.

18. Occasion immediately looses Furor and begins her usual taunting. Furor and Pyrochles immediately begin wrangling.

19. The "him" refers to Guyon. Occasion tries to get him into the mix, but Guyon stands fast and will not get angry. Notice how Spenser says that she could not entice Guyon to "impatience." Impatience is the beginning of fury. Temperance is patient.

22

Their fell contention still increaséd more,
And more thereby increased Furor's might,
That he his foe has hurt, and wounded sore,
And him in blood and dirt deforméd quite.
His mother eke°, more to augment his spite,   *also*
Now brought to him a flaming fire brand,
Which she in Stygian lake,[20] aye° burning bright,   *ever*
Had kindled: that she gave into his hand,
That armed with fire, more hardly he mote° him withstand.   *might*

23

Though 'gan that villain wax so fierce and strong,
That nothing might sustain his furious force;
He cast him down to ground, and all along
Drew him through dirt and mire without remorse,
And foully battered his comely corpse,
That Guyon much disdained so loathly sight.
At last he was compelled to cry perforce,
"Help, O Sir Guyon, help most noble knight,
To rid a wretched man from hands of hellish wight°."[21]   *creature*

24

The knight was greatly moved at his plaint,
And 'gan him dight° to succor° his distress,   *prepare / aid*
Till that the Palmer, by his grave restraint,
Him stayed from yielding pitiful redress;
And said, "Dear son, thy causeless ruth° repress,   *pity*
Nor let thy stout heart melt in pity vain:
He that his sorrow sought through willfulness,
And his foe fettered would release again,
Deserves to taste his follies' fruit, repented pain."[22]

---

20. "Stygian" refers to the river Styx, the entrance to the Greek underworld (i.e., she kindled the torch in the fires of hell).

21. The harder Pyrochles fights the harder he gets hit. Furor is the reflexive voodoo doll.

22. Guyon wants to help Pyrochles, but the Palmer stops him saying, "He needs to suffer for his foolishness. He wanted Occasion, let 'em have Furor. If you rescue him now, he'll only demand their release again." Temperance is knowing when to show mercy and when to show justice, and the wisdom to know when mercy will lead to true justice and justice lead to true mercy.

25

Guyon obeyed; So him away he drew
From needless trouble of renewing fight
Already fought, his voyage to pursue.
But rash Pyrochles' varlet°, Atin hight°,   *servant / named*
When late he saw his lord in heavy plight,
Under Sir Guyon's puissant° stroke to fall,   *mighty*
Him deeming dead, as then he seemed in sight,
Fled fast away, to tell his funeral
Unto his brother, whom Cymochles men did call.[23]

26

He was a man of rare redoubted° might,   *reverenced*
Famous throughout the world for warlike praise,
And glorious spoils, purchased in perilous fight:
Full many doughty° knights he in his days   *valiant*
Had done to death, subdued in equal frays°,   *fights*
Whose carcasses, for terror of his name,
Of fowls and beasts he made the piteous preys,
And hung their conquered arms for more defame
On gallow trees, in honor of his dearest dame.

27

His dearest dame is that enchantress,
The vile Acrasia, that with vain delights,
And idle pleasures in her Bower of Bliss,[24]
Does charm her lovers, and the feeble sprites°   *souls*
Can call out of the bodies of frail wights°:   *creatures*
Whom then she does transform to monstrous hues,
And horribly mis-shapes with ugly sights,
Captived eternally in iron mews°,   *cages*
And dark some dens, where Titan his face never shows.[25]

28

There Atin found Cymochles sojourning,
To serve his leman's° love: for he, by kind,   *lover's*

23. Atin had already left the scene earlier when Guyon first pinned Pyrochles. Atin
ran to find Cymochles, Pyrochles' brother.
24. The Bower of Bliss is of course the intended destination of Guyon. His mission
is to destroy that enchanted island. Now he has a chance to face the witch's boyfriend.
How exciting.
25. It's so bad the sun doesn't even dare let his light get down there.

Was given all to lust and loose living,
When ever his fierce hands he free might find:
And now he has poured out his idle mind
In dainty delices° and lavish joys,   *pleasures*
Having his warlike weapons cast behind,
And flows in pleasures, and vain pleasing toys,
Mingled amongst loose ladies and lascivious° boys.   *immoral*

29

And over him, art striving to compare
With nature, did an arbor green dispread°,   *extend*
Framed of wanton ivy, flowering fair,
Through which the fragrant eglantine[26] did spread
His pricking arms, entrailed with roses red,
Which dainty odors round about them threw,
And all within with flowers was garnished,
That when mild Zephyrus[27] amongst them blew,
Did breathe out bounteous smells and painted colors show.

30

And fast beside, there trickled softly down
A gentle stream, whose murmuring wave did play
Amongst the pumy° stones, and made a sound,   *glassy, lava*
To lull him soft a sleep, that by it lay;
The weary traveler, wandering that way,
Therein did often quench his thirsty heat,
And then by it his weary limbs display,
Whiles creeping slumber made him to forget
His former pain, and wiped away his toilsome sweat.

31

And on the other side a pleasant grove
Was shot up high, full of the stately tree,
That dedicated is to Olympic Jove,
And to his son Alcides, whenas he
Gained in Nemea goodly victory;
Therein the merry birds of every sort
Chanted aloud their cheerful harmony:

26. Webster says they're "Eurasian roses having prickly stems, fragrant leaves, bright pink flowers, and scarlet hips." Even though Cymochles is physically strong and has won many battles, he is a slave of his lusts and surrounded with dainty flowers. How sissy.
27. That's the god of the west wind.

And made amongst them selves a sweet consort,
That quickened the dull sprite with musical comfort.

32

There he him found all carelessly displayed,[28]
In secret shadow from the sunny ray,
On a sweet bed of lilies softly laid,
Amidst a flock of damsels fresh and gay,
That round about him dissolute° did play   *immoral*
Their wanton follies, and light merriment;
Every of which did loosely° disarray°   *immorally / uncover*
Her upper parts of meet° habiliments°,   *fitting / clothes*
And showed them naked, decked with many ornaments.

33

And every of them strove, with most delights,
Him to aggrate° and greatest pleasures show;   *please*
Some framed fair looks, glancing like evening lights,
Others sweet words, dropping like honey dew;
Some bathed kisses, and did soft embrew°,   *give*
The sugared liquor through his melting lips:
One boasts her beauty, and does yield to view
Her dainty limbs above her tender hips,
Another her out boasts, and all for trial strips.[29]

34

He, like an adder, lurking in the weeds,
His wandering thought in deep desire does steep,
And his frail eye with spoil of beauty feeds;
Sometimes he falsely feigns himself to sleep,
Whiles through their lids his wanton eyes do peep,
To steal a snatch of amorous conceit,
Whereby close fire into his heart does creep:
So, them deceives, deceived in his deceit,
Made drunk with drugs of dear voluptuous° receipt.[30]   *sensuous*

28. That's where Atin found Cymochles, lounging and sleeping.

29. Cymochles is surrounded by a gaggle of girls who are flirting with Cymochles and seeking his approval. Some of them seek his attention by uncovering everything and others seek it merely with their eyes. Immodesty is not merely "showing skin." It can occur with a glance of the eyes.

30. Cymochles has these women deceived. He plays their games and receives their passes eagerly.

35

Atin arriving there, when him he spied,
Thus in still waves of deep delight to wade,
Fiercely approaching, to him loudly cried,
"Cymochles; oh no, but Cymochles' shade,
In which that manly person late did fade,
What is become of great Acrates' son?
Or where hath he hung up his mortal blade,
That hath so many haughty conquests won?
Is all his force forlorn, and all his glory done?"

36

Then pricking him with his sharp-pointed dart°,   *dagger*
He said, "Up, up, thou womanish weak knight,[31]
That here in ladies' lap entombéd art,[32]
Unmindful of thy praise and prowest° might,   *powerful*
And weetless° eke° of lately wrought despite,   *thoughtless / also*
Whiles sad Pyrochles lies on senseless ground,
And groaneth out his utmost grudging sprite°,   *spirit*
Through many a stroke and many a streaming wound,
Calling thy help in vain, that here in joys art drowned."

37

Suddenly out of his delightful dream
The man awoke, and would have questioned more;
But he would not endure that woeful theme
For to dilate at large°, but urged sore   *explain at length*
With piercing words, and pitiful implore,
Him hasty to arise. As one affright°   *spooked*
With hellish fiends or Furies mad uproar,
He then up rose, inflamed with fell despite,
And called for his arms; for he would algates° fight.   *by all means*

31. This is a great line. The ambiguity stings. Cymochles is a "womanish weak knight'" by Atin's appraisal. The ambiguity is that we don't know if he is saying that Cymochles is weakened by women or is weak *like* a woman. But in the context, both seem to be intended. Obviously, this is not a slander against women in general. Rather it's an honest appraisal of immoral women. A loose woman is the weakest a woman can be. A woman's true strength and beauty is found in chastity. And being under the bondage of a loose woman is the weakest a man can be. His true strength is found in Christ-like leadership, not limp-wristed enchantment.

32. It's amusing that even Atin knows that sexual immorality is death. Cymochles is "entombed" in his sin.

38

They been ybrought; he quickly does him dight°,   *clad*
And lightly mounted, passeth on his way,
Nor ladies' loves, nor sweet entreaties might
Appease his heat, or hasty passage stay;
For he has vowed, to been avenged that day,
That day itself him seemed all too long:
On him, that did Pyrochles dear dismay:
So proudly pricketh° on his courser° strong,   *rode / horse*
And Atin aye° him pricks with spurs of shame and wrong.[33]   *ever*

33. As soon as Atin tells Cymochles that his brother has been defeated in battle, Cymochles is armed and off to battle. Atin continues mocking Cymochles all the way asking him why he has been lounging around while his brother has been fighting.

On Guard!

Directions: Identify where in the story the following quotes came from. Explain what they mean and their significance to the story.

1. "And henceforth by this day's ensample trow,
   That hasty wrath, and heedless hazardry,
   Do breed repentance late, and lasting infamy."

2. "The one," said she,
   "Because he won; the other because he
   Was won": So matter did she make of naught.

3. "Up, up, thou womanish weak knight,
   That here in ladies' lap entombéd art,
   Unmindful of thy praise and prowest might."

Canto VI.

Guyon is of immodest mirth,
led into loose desire,
Fights with Cymochles, whiles his bro-
ther burns in furious fire.

1

A harder lesson to learn continence°   *self-control*
In joyous pleasure, than in grievous pain:
or sweetness doth allure the weaker sense
So strongly, that uneaths° it can refrain   *beneath*
From that, which feeble nature covets feign;
But grief and wrath that be her enemies,
And foes of life, she better can restrain;
Yet virtue vaunts in both their victories,
And Guyon in them all shows goodly masteries.[1]

2

Whom bold Cymochles travelling to find,
With cruél purpose bent to wreak on him
The wrath, which Atin kindled in his mind,
Came to a river, by whose utmost brim

1. Spenser is saying that temptation is at its strongest when we are enjoying pleasures and sweetness. Sometimes grief, pain, and other kinds of hardship are our greatest
strengths and sources of wisdom. Solomon would agree (Eccl. 7:4). But simple virtue (i.e.,
righteousness) is the best weapon. And Guyon will show us how it's done.

Waiting to pass, he saw whereas did swim
Along the shore, as swift as glance of eye,
A little gondola, bedecked trim
With boughs and arbors woven cunningly,
That like a little forest seeméd outwardly.

3

And therein sat a lady fresh and fair,
Making sweet solace to herself alone;
Sometimes she sung, as loud as lark in air,
Sometimes she laughed that nigh her breath was gone,
Yet was there not with her else anyone,
That might to her move cause of merriment:
Matter of mirth enough, though there were none
She could devise, and thousand ways invent,
To feed her foolish humor, and vain jolliment.[2]

4

Which when far off Cymochles heard and saw,
He loudly called to such as were aboard,
The little bark° unto the shore to draw,   *boat*
And him to ferry over that deep ford:
The merry mariner[3] unto his word
Soon hearkened, and her painted boat straightway
Turned to the shore where that same warlike lord
She in received; but Atin by no way
She would admit, albe° the knight her much did pray.[4]   *even though*

5

Eftsoones° her shallow ship away did slide,   *soon*
More swift, than swallow shears the liquid sky,
Withouten oar or pilot it to guide,
Or wingéd canvas with the wind to fly,
Only she turned a pin, and by and by
It cut away upon the yielding wave,
Nor cared she her course for to apply:

2. Meet Phaedria. She laughs and giggles about everything. Sometimes her shoelaces are funny.

3. Phaedria is the "merry mariner," although Ichiro would also qualify for the title.

4. She takes Cymochles but denies passage to Atin. Kind of suspicious if you ask me, not allowing any friends to go along.

For it was taught the way, which she would have,
And both from rocks and flats itself could wisely save.

6

And all the way, the wanton damsel found
New mirth, her passenger to entertain:
For she in pleasant purpose did abound,
And greatly joyéd merry tales to feign,
Of which a store-house did with her remain,
Yet seeméd, nothing well they her became;
For all her words she drowned with laughter vain,
And wanted grace in uttering of the same,
That turned all her pleasance to a scoffing game.[5]

7

And other whiles vain toys° she would devise   *games*
As her fantastic wit did most delight,
Sometimes her head she fondly would aguise°   *adorn*
With gaudy garlands, or fresh flowerets dight°   *decked*
About her neck, or rings of rushes plight°;   *braid*
Sometimes to do him laugh, she would assay°   *pretend*
To laugh at shaking of the leaves light,
Or to behold the water work and play
About her little frigate° therein making way.   *boat*

8

Her light behavior, and loose dalliance°   *flirting*
Gave wondrous great contentment to the knight,
That of his way he had no sovenance°,   *care*
Nor care of vowed revenge, and cruél fight,
But to weak wench did yield his martial might.
So easy was to quench his flaméd mind
With one sweet drop of sensual delight:
So easy is, to appease the stormy wind
Of malice in the calm of pleasant womankind.[6]

5. She sails with Cymochles, laughing all the way. But her merriment is obnoxious and hardly funny.

6. After only a few minutes of Phaedria's goofiness, Cymochles has completely forgotten what he was upset about. He's once again a "womanish weak knight."

9

Diverse discourses in their way they spent,
'Mongst which Cymochles of her questionéd,
Both what she was and what that usage meant,
Which in her cot she daily practicéd.
"Vain man," said she, "that wouldest be reckonéd
A stranger in thy home and ignorant
Of Phaedria, for so my name is read,
Of Phaedria, thine own fellow servant;
For thou to serve Acrasia thyself doest vaunt°.[7]   *boast*

10

"In this wide inland sea, that hight by name
The Idle Lake, my wandering ship I row,
That knows her port, and thither sails by aim,
Nor care, nor fear I, how the wind do blow,
Or whether swift I wend or whether slow:
Both slow and swift a like do serve my turn°,   *aim*
Nor swelling Neptune, nor loud thundering Jove
Can change my cheer, or make me ever mourn;
My little boat can safely pass this perilous bourne°."[8]   *stream, river*

11

Whiles thus she talked and whiles thus she toyed,
They were far past the passage, which he spake,
And come unto an island waste and void,
That floated in the midst of that great lake:
There her small gondola her port did make,
And that gay pair issuing on the shore
Disburdened her. Their way they forward take
Into the land, that lay them fair before,
Whose pleasance she him showed and plentiful great store.[9]

12

It was a chosen plot of fertile land,
Amongst wide waves set, like a little nest,

7. Phaedria is friends with Acrasia.
8. Two things: The name of this particular body of water is the Idle Lake. Also, Cymochles represents a completely unbalanced man. His name means "wave." Just picture a wave going up and down, up and down. That's Cymochles.
9. The boat takes them far beyond where Cymochles had originally asked to be taken. But as you can see, he hasn't the slightest concern about this.

As if it had by nature's cunning hand,
Been choicely picked out from all the rest,
And laid forth for ensample of the best:
No dainty flower or herb that grows on ground,
No arboret° with painted blossoms dressed,   *garden*
And smelling sweet, but there it might be found
To bud out fair and her sweet smells throw all around.

13

No tree, whose branches did not bravely spring;
No branch whereon a fine bird did not sit:
No bird but did her shrill notes sweetly sing;
No song but did contain a lovely dit°:   *sound*
Trees, branches, birds, and songs were fraoméd fit,
For to allure frail mind to careless ease.[10]
Careless the man soon wax° and his weak wit   *became*
Was overcome of thing that did him please;
So pleaséd, did his wrathful purpose fair appease.

14

Thus when she had his eyes and senses fed
With false delights, and filled with pleasures vain,
Into a shady dale she soft him led,
And laid him down upon a grassy plain;
And her sweet self without dread or disdain,
She set beside, laying his head disarmed
In her loose lap, it softly to sustain,
Where soon he slumbered, fearing not be harmed,
The whiles with a love lay° she thus him sweetly charmed.[11]   *song*

15

"Behold, O man, that toilsome pains doest take
The flowers, the fields, and all that pleasant grows,
How they themselves do thine ensample make,
Whiles nothing envious nature them forth throws
Out of her fruitful lap; how, no man knows,
They spring, they bud, they blossom fresh and fair,

---

10. Every flower, tree, bird, or song is like shiny plastic—perfect to frail minds. Insert Thomas Kinkade picture here.

11. Phaedria takes Cymochles into a grove and lays him down, then begins to sing a love song to him. Yuck.

And deck the world with their rich pompous shows;
Yet no man for them taketh pains or care,
Yet no man to them can his careful pains compare.

16

"The lily, lady of the flowering field,
The flower-de-luce°, her lovely paramour°,   *flower-of-light / lover*
Bid thee to them thy fruitless labors yield,
And soon leave off this toilsome weary store;
Lo, lo how brave she decks her bounteous bower,
With silken curtains and gold coverlets,
Therein to shroud her sumptuous belamour°,   *lover*
Yet neither spins nor cards°, nor cares nor frets,   *brushes*
But to her mother nature all her care she lets.[12]

17

"Why then dost thou, O man, that of them all
Art lord, and eke° of nature sovereign,   *also*
Willfully make thyself a wretched thrall°,   *slave*
And waste thy joyous hours in needless pain,
Seeking for danger and adventures vain?
What boots° it all to have, and nothing use?   *avails*
Who shall him rue° that swimming in the main,   *pity*
Will die for thirst, and water doth refuse?
Refuse such fruitless toil and present pleasures choose."[13]

18

By this she had him lulled fast asleep,
That of no worldly thing he care did take;
Then she with liquors strong his eyes did steep°,   *wash*
That nothing should him hastily awake:
So she him left, and did herself betake
Unto her boat again, with which she cleft
The slothful wave of that great grisly lake;

12. This "charm" should sound familiar. Only something's not right. (Read Matthew 6:25–34.) These last couple of stanzas portray Phaedria as the "minister" of a false gospel. She speaks many of the same exhortations as Christ, only her god is empty and idle pleasure and not our heavenly Father who gives the fullness of joy at whose right hand are pleasures forevermore. Jesus gives contentment and peace, but sluggards and idlers will not inherit the kingdom.

13. I.e., "Give up your adventures and fighting. Relax and be at ease here."

Soon she that island far behind her left,
And now is come to that same place where first she weft°.   *floated*

19

By this time was the worthy Guyon brought
Unto the other side of that wide strand°,   *beach*
Where she was rowing, and for passage sought:
Him needed not long call, she soon to hand
Her ferry brought, where him she bidding fond,[14]
With his sad guide; himself she took aboard,
But the black Palmer suffered still to stand,
Nor would for price or prayers once afford,
To ferry that old man over the perilous ford.[15]

20

Guyon was loath to leave his guide behind,
Yet being entered might not back retire;
For the flit° bark°, obeying to her mind,   *swift / boat*
Forth launched quickly, as she did desire,
Nor gave him leave to bid that agéd sire
Adieu, but nimbly ran her wonted° course   *accustomed*
Through the dull billows thick as troubled mire,
Whom neither wind out of their seat could force,
Nor timely tides did drive out of their sluggish source.

21

And by the way, as was her wonted guise,
Her merry fit she freshly 'gan to rear,
And did of joy and jollity devise,
Herself to cherish, and her guest to cheer:
The knight was courteous, and did not forbear
Her honest mirth and pleasance to partake;
But when he saw her toy, and gibe, and gear,
And pass the bonds of modest merry-make,
Her dalliance he despised, and follies did forsake.[16]

14. She's "happy" as always.

15. You'll notice that friends simply aren't allowed. Phaedria only preys on victims who are alone. This isn't surprising since she's interested in the empty joys of idleness. Idleness is the friend of solitude.

16. At first Guyon is polite and courteous, but when he realizes she's a flirtatious ditz, he wants nothing to do with her.

22

Yet she still followed her former style,
And said, and did all that mote° him delight,   *might*
Till they arrivéd in that pleasant isle,
Where sleeping late she left her other knight.
But when as Guyon of that land had sight,
He wist° himself amiss, and angry said;   *knew*
"Ah dame, perdy° ye have not done me right,   *truly*
Thus to mislead me, whiles I you obeyed:
Me little needed from my right way to have strayed."[17]

23

"Fair sir," quoth she, "be not displeased at all;
Who fares on sea, may not command his way,
Nor wind and weather at his pleasure call:
The sea is wide, and easy for to stray;
The wind unstable, and doth never stay.
But here a while ye may in safety rest,
Till season serve new passage to assay°;   *go*
Better safe port, than be in seas distressed."[18]
Therewith she laughed and did her earnest end in jest.

24

But he half discontent, mote° natheless°   *might / nevertheless*
Himself appease, and issued forth on shore:
The joys whereof and happy fruitfulness,
Such as he saw, she 'gan him lay before,
And all though pleasant, yet she made much more:
The fields did laugh, the flowers did freshly spring,
The trees did bud, and early blossoms bore,
And all the choir of birds did sweetly sing,
And told that garden's pleasures in their caroling.

25

And she more sweet, than any bird on bough,
Would oftentimes amongst them bear a part,
And strive to pass as she could well enough
Their native music by her skillful art:

17. Guyon notices right away that she has brought him away from where he wanted to go. He's not too happy.
18. I.e., "Omigosh, really? Gee, I'm sorry. You never can tell with the seas. They just take you wherever they want."

So did she all, that might his constant heart
Withdraw from thought of warlike enterprise,
And drown in dissolute delights apart,
Where noise of arms, or view of martial guise
Might not revive desire of knightly exercise.

26

But he was wise and wary of her will,
And ever held his hand upon his heart:
Yet would not seem so rude and thewed ill°,   *ill-mannered*
As to despise so courteous seeming part,
That gentle lady did to him impart,
But fairly tempering fond desire subdued,
And ever her desired to depart.[19]
She list° not hear, but her disports° pursued,   *would / diversions*
And ever bade him stay till time the tide renewed.

27

And now by this, Cymochles' hour was spent,
That he awoke out of his idle dream,
And shaking off his drowsy dreariment,
'Gan him avize° how ill did him beseem,   *realize*
In slothful sleep his molten heart to steam,
And quench the brand of his conceivéd ire°.   *wrath*
Though up he started, stirred with shame extreme,
Nor stayed for his damsel to inquire,
But marched to the strand°, their passage to require.[20]   *beach*

28

And in the way he with Sir Guyon met,
Accompanied with Phaedria the fair,
Eftsoones° he 'gan to rage and inly° fret,   *shortly / inwardly*
Crying, "Let be that lady debonair°,   *good*
Thou recreant° knight, and soon thyself prepare   *faithless coward*
To battle, if thou mean her love to gain:[21]
Lo, lo already, how the fowls in air

19. He tries to remain polite, but he regularly reminds her that he would like to be taken back.
20. Cymochles wakes up and quickly realizes that he's been thwarted from his original plan and rushes to the beach to seek passage back across the lake.
21. Cymochles is ready to fight for the girl (Phaedria).

Do flock, awaiting shortly to obtain
Thy carcass for their prey, the guerdon° of thy pain."   *reward*

29

And there with all he fiercely at him flew,
And with importune outrage him assailed;
Who soon prepared to field his sword forth drew,
And him with equal value countervailed:[22]
Their mighty strokes their habergeons[23] dismailed,
And naked made each other's manly spalls°;   *shoulders*
The mortal steel dispiteously entailed°   *cut*
Deep in their flesh, quite through the iron walls,
That a large purple stream down their jambeux° falls.   *shin-guards*

30

Cymochles, that had never met before
So puissant° foe, with envious despite   *valiant*
His proud presuméd force increaséd more,
Disdaining to be held so long in fight;
Sir Guyon grudging not so much his might,
As those unknightly railings, which he spoke,
With wrathful fire his courage kindled bright,
Thereof devising shortly to be wroke°,   *avenged*
And doubling all his powers, redoubled every stroke.[24]

31

Both of them high at once their hands enhanced°,   *raised*
And both at once their huge blows down did sway;
Cymochles sword on Guyon's shield yglanced,
And thereof nigh one quarter sheared away;
But Guyon's angry blade so fierce did play
On the other's helmet, which as Titan[25] shone,
That quite it clove his plumed crest in twain°,   *two*
And baréd all his head unto the bone;
Wherewith astonished still he stood as senseless stone.[26]

22. He fights back.
23. These are sleeveless coats of mail.
24. So Cymochles is upset because Guyon is such a great warrior, and Guyon is upset because Cymochles keeps running his mouth.
25. This refers to either the Titan gods of Greek myth or the largest moon of Saturn. Take your pick. It's big and it's bright, either way.
26. That's what we call a close shave.

32

Still as he stood, fair Phaedria that beheld
That deadly danger, soon atween° them ran;   *between*
And at their feet herself most humbly felled,²⁷
Crying with piteous voice, and countenance wan°;   *pale*
"Ah well away, most noble lords, how can
Your cruél eyes endure so piteous sight,
To shed your lives on ground? Woe worth° the man,   *worthless*
That first did teach the curséd steel to bite
In his own flesh and make way to the living sprite°.   *spirit*

33

"If ever love of lady did empierce
Your iron breasts or pity could find place,
Withhold your bloody hands from battle fierce,
And since for me ye fight, to me this grace
Both yield, to stay your deadly strife a space."
They stayed a while: and forth she 'gan proceed:
"Most wretched woman, and of wicked race,
That am the author of this heinous deed,
And cause of death between two doughty° knights do breed.   *valiant*

34

"But if for me ye fight, or me will serve,
Not this rude kind of battle nor these arms
Are meet°, the which do men in bale° to starve,   *right / misery*
And doleful sorrow heap with deadly harms:
Such cruél game my scarmoges° disarms: *skirmishes*
Another war and other weapons I
Do love, where love does give his sweet alarms,
Without bloodshed, and where the enemy
Does yield unto his foe a pleasant victory.²⁸

35

"Debateful strife and cruél enmity
The famous name of knighthood foully shined;²⁹

27. Who does Phaedria remind you of? She is a false Medina. Remember how Medina attempted to break up the knights who fought earlier? Keep reading.

28. Phaedria's slogan is familiar to us: "Make love not war." But Spenser is making the point that pacifism is a kind of idleness. True temperance discerns when it is right and proper to fight.

29. I.e., "Knighthood has wrongly glamorized fighting."

But lovely peace and gentle amity°,   *friendship*
And in amours° the passing hours to spend,   *loves*
The mighty martial hands do most commend;
Of love they ever greater glory bore,
Than of their arms: Mars is Cupid's friend,
And is for Venus' loves renownéd more,
Than all his wars and spoils, the which he did of yore°."[30]   *long ago*

36

Therewith she sweetly smiled. They though full bent,
To prove extremities of bloody fight,[31]
Yet at her speech their rages 'gan relent,
And calm the sea of their tempestuous spite,
Such power have pleasing words: such is the might
Of courteous clemency in gentle heart.
Now after all was ceased, the faerie knight[32]
Besought that damsel suffer him depart,
And yield him ready passage to that other part.

37

She no less glad, than he desirous was
Of his departure thence; for of her joy
And vain delight she saw he light did pass,
A foe of folly and immodest toy,
Still solemn sad or still disdainful coy,
Delighting all in arms and cruél war,
That her sweet peace and pleasures did annoy,
Troubled with terror and unquiet jar,
That she well pleased was thence to remove him far.[33]

38

Though him she brought aboard, and her swift boat
Forthwith directed to that further strand°;   *shore*
The which on the dull waves did lightly float
And soon arrivéd on the shallow sand,

---

30. Mars is the god of war and Cupid a god of love. Venus is the mother of Cupid. Phaedria is claiming that the offspring of Venus is far greater than any daring deed of Mars.

31. They both want to fight it out.

32. That's Guyon.

33. She wants him to go as much as he wants to leave. She realized it was no use. Guyon wasn't into her games. He is a warrior.

Where glad-some Guyon sallied forth to land,
And to that damsel thanks gave for reward.
Upon that shore he spied Atin stand,
There by his master left, when late he fared
In Phaedria's flit bark° over that perilous shard.[34]   *boat*

39
Well could he him remember, since of late
He with Pyrochles' sharp debatement made;
Straight 'gan he him revile and bitter rate,[35]
As shepherd's cur°, that in dark evening's shade   *dog*
Hath tracked forth some savage beast's trade;[36]
"Vile miscreant°," said he, "whither doest thou fly   *villain*
The shame and death, which will thee soon invade?
What coward hand shall do thee next to die,
That art thus foully fled from famous enemy?"

40
With that he stiffly shook his steelhead dart:
But sober Guyon, hearing him so rail,
Though somewhat movéd in his mighty heart,
Yet with strong reason mastered passion frail,
And passéd fairly forth. He turning tail,
Back to the strand° retired, and there still stayed,   *shore*
Awaiting passage, which him late did fail;
The whiles Cymochles with that wanton maid
The hasty heat of his avowed revenge delayed.[37]

41
Whilst there the varlet[38] stood, he saw from far
An armed knight that towards him fast ran,
He ran on foot, as if in luckless war
His forlorn steed from him the victor won;
He seemed breathless, heartless, faint, and wan°,   *pale*

34. Atin is standing right where he had been left by his master Cymochles, when he first went with Phaedria.
35. Atin remembers Guyon and proceeds to call him names.
36. That's a good insult.
37. Guyon refuses to let himself be angered by Atin's insults. He leaves and waits for a different passage across the lake. Meanwhile Phaedria continues to sweet talk Cymochles. She tells him knock-knock jokes. She laughs hysterically. He laughs too.
38. Remember, that's Atin.

And all his armor sprinkled was with blood,
And soiled with dirty gore, that no man can
Discern the hew thereof. He never stood,
But bent his hasty course towards the idle flood.

42

The varlet° saw, when to the flood he came,   *page*
How without stop or stay he fiercely leaped,
And deep himself be-dunked in the same,
That in the lake his lofty crest was steeped,
Nor of his safety seemed care he kept,
But with his raging arms he rudely flashed,
The waves about, and all his armor swept,
That all the blood and filth away was washed,
Yet still he beat the water, and the billows dashed.[39]

43

Atin drew nigh, to weet what it mote° be;[40]   *might*
For much he wondered at that uncouth sight;
Whom should he, but his own dear lord there see,
His own dear lord, Pyrochles, in sad plight,
Ready to drown himself for fell despite.
"Harrow° now out, and well away," he cried,   *pull*
"What dismal day hath lent this curséd light,
To see my lord so deadly damnified°   *damned, destroyed*
Pyrochles, O Pyrochles, what is thee betide?"[41]

44

"I burn, I burn, I burn,"[42] then loud he cried,
"O how I burn with implacable° fire,   *unending*
Yet nought can quench mine inly° flaming side,   *inwardly*
Nor sea of liquor cold, nor lake of mire,
Nothing but death can do me to respire."[43]
"Ah be it," said he, "from Pyrochles far
After pursuing death once to require,

39. While Atin is still busy spewing filth, a knight comes running at full speed covered in dirt and blood and dives into the lake and splashes around like a madman. Who's this?
40. Atin goes over to see what's going on.
41. I.e., "What's the matter?"
42. Do you think he burns?
43. The fire is so bad that only death can cure him (he believes).

Or think, that ought those puissant° hands may mar: *mighty*
Death is for wretches born under unhappy star."[44]

45

"Perdy°, then is it fit for me," said he,   *truly*
"That am, I ween°, most wretched man alive,   *know*
Burning in flames, yet no flames can I see,
And dying daily, daily yet revive:
O Atin, help to me last death to give."
The varlet° at his plaint was grieved so sore,   *page*
That his deep wounded heart in two did rive°,   *split*
And his own health remembering now no more,
Did follow that ensample, which he blamed afore.

46

Into the lake he leapt, his lord to aid,
So love the dread of danger doth despise
And of him catching hold him strongly stayed
From drowning. But more happy he, than wise
Of that sea's nature did him not advise.[45]
The waves thereof so slow and sluggish were,
Engrossed with mud, which did them foul agrise°,   *loathe*
That every weighty thing they did upbear°,   *hold up*
Nor ought° mote° ever sink down to the bottom there.[46]   *anything / might*

47

Whiles thus they struggled in that idle wave,
And strove in vain, the one himself to drown,
The other both from drowning for to save,
Lo, to that shore one in an ancient gown,
Whose hoary locks great gravity did crown,
Holding in hand a goodly arming sword,
By fortune came, led with the troublous sown:
Where drenchéd deep he found in that dull ford
The careful servant, striving with his raging lord.[47]

44. I.e., "You're too great to die. Death is for unlucky wretches."
45. I.e., he was unaware of the nature of the sea.
46. This is what you might call a bog. Things don't sink; it's too thick with slime and mud.
47. So Pyrochles is trying to drown himself, Atin is trying to save the both of them, and an old man arrives with a sword. Who's this old man, do you think?

48

Him Atin spying knew right well of yore,
And loudly called, "Help, help, O Archimage;
To save my lord, in wretched plight forlore°;   *lost*
Help with thy hand, or with thy counsel sage:
Weak hands, but counsel is most strong in age."
Him when the old man saw, he wondered sore,
To see Pyrochles there so rudely rage:
Yet sithens° help, he saw, he needed more   *since*
Than pity, he in haste approached to the shore.

49

And called, "Pyrochles, what is this, I see?
What hellish fury hath at earst thee hent?[48]
Furious ever I thee knew to be,
Yet never in this strange astonishment."
"These flames, these flames," he cried, "do me torment."
"What flames," quoth he, "when I thee present see,
In danger rather to be drowned, than burnt?"
"Harrow°, the flames, which me consume," said he.   *Help!*
"Nor can be quenched within my secret bowels be."[49]

50

"That cursèd man, that cruel fiend of hell,
Furor, oh Furor, hath me thus bedight°:   *done this*
His deadly wounds within my livers swell,
And his hot fire burns in mine entrails bright,
Kindled through his infernal brand of spite,
Since late with him I battle vain would boast;   *since*
That now I ween° Jove's dreaded thunder light   *think*
Does scorch not half so sore, nor damnèd ghost
In flaming Phlegeton[50] does not so fell-y roast.[51]

48. I.e., "What's got hold of you?"

49. Did you catch that? Turns out that the old man is Archimago. Remember, Archimago went to fetch Arthur's sword for Braggadochio. Archimago asks what the trouble is, and Pyrochles says that he's being burned. Archimago says it looks more like he's about to be drowned, but Pyrochles explains that it's a burning in his insides. Furor, he will go on to explain, is the source of his agony.

50. That's an infamous and infernal burning river. No toe dabbling.

51. I.e., "Lightning and Hell are not as bad as the burning in my body."

51

Which when as Archimago heard, his grief
He knew right well, and him at once disarmed:
Then searched his secret wounds, and made a proof°   *inspection*
Of every place, that was with bruising harmed,
Or with the hidden fire too inly° warmed.   *inwardly*
Which done, he balms and herbs thereto applied,
And evermore with mighty spells them charmed,
That in short space he has them qualified°,   *treated*
And him restored to health, that would have algates° died.[52]   *surely*

52. Archimago pulls Pyrochles from the lake and treats his wounds and pain with herbs and spells.

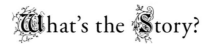 What's the Story?

Directions: Identify where in the story the following quotes came from. Explain what they mean and their significance to the story.

1. "And all the way, the wanton damsel found
   New mirth, her passenger to entertain."

2. "Mars is Cupid's friend."

3. "Whiles thus they struggled in that idle wave,
   And strove in vain, the one himself to drown,
   The other both from drowning for to save."

Canto VII.

Guyon finds Mammon in a delve°,   *ravine*
Sunning his treasure hore°:   *hoard*
Is by him tempted and led down,
To see his secret store.

1

As pilot well expert in perilous wave,
That to a steadfast star his course hath bent,
When foggy mists, or cloudy tempests have
The faithful light of that fair lamp blent°,   *blurred*
And covered heaven with hideous dreariment,
Upon his card° and compass firms his eye,   *chart*
The masters of his long experiment,
And to them does the steady helm apply,
Bidding his wingéd vessel fairly forward fly.

2

So Guyon having lost his trusty guide,
Late left beyond that Idle Lake, proceeds
Yet on his way, of none accompanied;[1]
And evermore himself with comfort feeds,

---

1. Guyon was forced to part with the Palmer when he hitched a ride with Phaedria, so now Guyon continues on his quest, alone for the present.

Of his own virtues and praiseworthy deeds.[2]
So long he rode[3], yet no adventure found,
Which fame of her shrill trumpet worthy reads°:   *tells*
For still he traveled through wide wasteful ground,
That naught but desert wilderness showed all around.

3

At last he came unto a gloomy glade,
Covered with boughs and shrubs from heaven's light,
Whereas he sitting found in secret shade
An uncouth, savage, and uncivil wight°,   *creature*
Of grisly hue, and foul ill favored sight;
His face with smoke was tanned, and eyes were bleared,
His head and beard with soot were ill bedight°,   *covered*
His coal-black hands did seem to have been seared
In smith's fire-spitting forge, and nails like claws appeared.[4]

4

His iron coat all overgrown with rust,
Was underneath enveloped with gold,
Whose glistering gloss darkened with filthy dust,
Well it appeared to have been of old
A work of rich entail and curious mould,
Woven with antics° and wild imagery: *pictures*
And in his lap a mass of coin he told°,   *had*
And turnéd upside down, to feed his eye
A covetous desire with his huge treasury.

5

And round about him lay on every side
Great heaps of gold that never could be spent:

2. This may sound uncomfortable to modern pietistic ears. However, Spenser describes the Christian knight not glorying in empty or vain conceits; rather he is showing the Christian knight obeying the Word of God. Galatians 6:3–5 says: "For if a man think himself to be something, when he is nothing, he deceiveth himself. But let every man prove his own work, and then shall he have rejoicing in himself alone, and not in another." Guyon overcame the wiles of Phaedria and Pyrochles, and he and every Christian ought to rejoice in the honest appraisal of our own "virtues and praiseworthy deeds" (cf. 2 Cor. 13:5).

3. Either Guyon found his old horse, got a new horse, borrowed one, or Spenser forgot that Guyon is missing his. Or he's riding a Harley Davidson.

4. This fellow that Guyon meets is covered in soot and dirt. We will call him Mr. Chimney-face. He played with one too many sticks of dynamite it seems.

Of which some were rude ore, not purified
Of Mulciber's[5] devouring element;
Some others were new driven and distent°   *drawn out*
Into great ingoes°[6], and to wedges square;   *ingots*
Some in round plates withouten monument°;   *identification*
But most were stamped and in their metal bare
The antique shapes of kings and Caesars strange and rare.

6

Soon as he Guyon saw, in great affright
And haste he rose for to remove aside
Those precious hills from stranger's envious sight,
And down them poured through an hole full wide,
Into the hollow earth, them there to hide.
But Guyon lightly to him leaping, stayed°   *held back*
His hand, that trembled, as one terrified;
And though himself were at the sight dismayed,
Yet him perforce° restrained, and to him doubtful said.[7]   *by necessity*

7

"What art thou man, if man at all thou art,
That here in desert hast thine habitance°,   *home*
And these rich heaps of wealth doest hide apart
From the world's eye and from her right usance°?"[8]   *use*
Thereat with staring eyes fixed askance°,   *suspiciously*
In great disdain, he answered, "Hardy elf,
That darest view my direful° countenance,   *ugly*
I read° thee rash, and heedless of thyself,   *say*
To trouble my still seat and heaps of precious pelf°.   *riches*

8

"God of the world and worldlings I me call,
Great Mammon,[9] greatest god below the sky,

5. Mulciber is also known as Vulcan, a god of fire. Here it refers to pieces of gold and silver that have not yet been purified in a furnace and shaped into coinage.

6. An ingot is a standard shape metal is cast into.

7. When Guyon arrives, Mr. Chimney-face starts pushing his hoard of treasure into a great hole in the ground. But Guyon quickly stops him.

8. Guyon wonders why all this wealth is being roosted on in the middle of the desert. Why is it not being put to its proper use?

9. Mr. Chimney-face has a name! Meet Mammon. Mammon is of course the god of fading worldly goods and treasures. This canto is connected to the last one by its theme of Christ's Sermon on the Mount (cf. Mt. 6:19–24).

That of my plenty pour out unto all,
And unto none my graces do envy:
Riches, renown, and principality,
Honor, estate, and all this world's good,
For which men swink° and sweat incessantly,   *work*
For me do flow into an ample flood,
And in the hollow earth have their eternal brood.[10]

9

"Wherefore if me thou deign to serve and sue°,   *pursue*
At thy command lo all these mountains be;
Or if to thy great mind, or greedy view
All these may not suffice, there shall to thee
Ten times so much be numbered frank and free."
"Mammon," said he, "thy godhead's vaunt is vain,
And idle offers of thy golden fee;
To them, that covet such eye-glutting gain,
Proffer° thy gifts, and fitter servants entertain.   *give*

10

"Me ill besits,[11] that in der-doing° arms,   *valiant-fighting*
And honor's suit° my vowed days do spend,   *pursuit*
Unto thy bounteous baits and pleasing charms,
With which weak men thou witchest°, to attend: *enchant*
Regard of worldly muck doth foully blend°,   *corrupt*
And low abase the high heroic sprite°,   *spirit*
That joys for crowns and kingdoms to contend;
Fair shields, gay steeds, bright arms be my delight:
Those be the riches fit for an adventurous knight."[12]

11

"Vain glorious elf,"[13] said he, "doest not thou weet°,   *know*
That money can thy wants at will supply?
Shields, steeds, and arms, and all things for thee meet°   *needed*
It can purvey° in twinkling of an eye;   *provide*

---

10. Men are welcome to his hoard as long they realize that all these goods are ultimately his.

11. I.e., "It is not fitting for me . . ."

12. Notice that Guyon doesn't say he doesn't want *anything*. Rather, he says that he wants the marks of knighthood and valor. Temperance isn't a lack of desire; it is desiring truly desirable things.

13. Mammon is calling Guyon "elf."

And crowns and kingdoms to thee multiply.
Do not I kings create, and throw the crown
Sometimes to him, that low in dust doth lie?
And him that reigned, into his room thrust down,
And whom I lust° do heap with glory and renown?"   *want*

12

"All otherwise,"[14] said he, "I riches read°,   *know*
And deem them root of all disquietness;
First got with guile, and then preserved with dread,
And after spent with pride and lavishness,
Leaving behind them grief and heaviness.
Infinite mischiefs of them do arise,
Strife; and debate, bloodshed, and bitterness,
Outrageous wrong, and hellish covetous,
That noble heart as great dishonor doth despise.[15]

13

"Nor thine be kingdoms, nor the scepters thine;
But realms and rulers thou doest both confound,
And loyal truth to treason doest incline;
Witness the guiltless blood poured oft on ground,
The crownéd often slain, the slayer crowned,
The sacred diadem in pieces rent,
And purple robe gored with many a wound;
Castles surprised, great cities sacked and burnt:
So makest thou kings, and gainest wrongful government.[16]

14

"Long were to tell the troublous storms that toss
The private state, and make the life unsweet:
Who swelling sails in Caspian Sea doth cross,
And in frail wood on Adrian gulf doth fleet°,   *float*
Doth not, I ween°, so many evils meet."[17]   *think*

14. I.e., "Just the opposite . . ." This is Guyon responding to Mammon.

15. I.e., "In fact there are so many downsides to great riches, a noble heart counts them a dishonor."

16. Mammon has been trying to convince Guyon of his authority and power, but Guyon is strong. He isn't buying it. He knows that Mammon is only the source of envy, greed, and covetousness, resulting in bloodshed.

17. I.e., "It's safer to sail the stormy seas on a popsicle stick than to live with great riches."

Then Mammon waxing wroth,[18] "And why then," said,
"Are mortal men so fond and indiscreet,
So evil thing to seek unto their aid,
And having not complain, and having it upbraid?"[19]

15

"Indeed," quoth he, "through foul intemperance,
Frail men are oft captived to covetous:
But would they think, with how small allowance
Untroubled Nature doth her self suffice,
Such superfluities° they would despise,   *luxuries, extras*
Which with sad cares impeach our native joys:
At the well head the purest streams arise:
But mucky filth his branching arms annoys,
And with uncomely weeds the gentle wave accloys°.[20]   *clogs*

16

"The antique world, in his first flowering youth,
Found no defect in his Creator's grace,
But with glad thanks and unreprovéd truth,
The gifts of sovereign bounty did embrace:
Like angels' life was then men's happy case;
But later ages pride, like corn-fed steed,
Abused her plenty, and fat swollen increase
To all licentious lust, and 'gan exceed
The measure of her mean and natural first need.

17

"Then 'gan a curséd hand the quiet womb
Of his great grandmother with steel to wound,
And the hid treasures in her sacred tomb,
With sacrilege to dig.[21] Therein he found
Fountains of gold and silver to abound,

18. Mammon, getting mad.

19. I.e., "Then why do men want it so badly?" Mammon asks, "Why do they complain without it and whine when they have it?"

20. Guyon says that men do often covet Mammon's filth, but if they only realized how all of their needs are taken care of, they wouldn't desire excess riches which tend to defile and confuse the good and simple life.

21. Great grandmother is the earth. They were mining for gold and silver. Greed. Obviously it's not wrong to mine or look for gold. God put gold into the world for us to find and use (e.g., Gen. 2:11–12). But Guyon is talking about those early men who because of their lust and greed sought such treasures.

Of which the matter of his huge desire
And pompous pride eftsoones° he did compound;   *swiftly*
Then avarice 'gan through his veins inspire
His greedy flames, and kindled life-devouring fire."

18

"Son," said he then, "let be thy bitter scorn,
And leave the rudeness of that antique age
To them, that lived therein in state forlorn;
Thou that doest live in later times, must wage
Thy works for wealth, and life for gold engage.
If then thee list° my offered grace to use,   *want*
Take what thou please of all this surplusage°;   *riches*
If thee list° not leave° have thou to refuse: *want / permission*
But thing refused, do not afterward accuse."[22]

19

"Me list° not," said the Elfin knight,[23] "receive   *want*
Thing offered, till I know it well be got,
Nor wote° I, but thou didst these goods bereave°   *know / stole*
From rightful owner by unrighteous lot,
Or that blood guiltiness or guile them blot."
"Perdy°," quoth he, "yet never eye did view,   *truly*
Nor tongue did tell, nor hand these handled not,
But safe I have them kept in secret mew°,   *storage*
From heaven's sight, and power of all which them pursue."

20

"What secret place," quoth he, "can safely hold
So huge a mass, and hide from heaven's eye?[24]
Or where hast thou thy won°, that so much gold   *home*
Thou canst preserve from wrong and robbery?"
"Come thou," quoth he, "and see." So by and by
Through that thick covert° he him led, and found   *thicket*
A dark-some way, which no man could descry°,   *see*
That deep descended through the hollow ground,
And was with dread and horror compassed around.[25]

22. I.e., "If you don't want any, fine. But don't say I didn't give you a chance."
23. Guyon is the Elfin knight, of course.
24. I.e., "Where can you hide something from heaven?"
25. Mammon says he'll give Guyon a tour of his underground lair, and Guyon follows him into the shadows.

21

At length they came into a larger space,
That stretched itself into an ample plain,
Through which a beaten broad highway did trace,
That straight did lead to Pluto's grisly reign:[26]
By that way's side, there sat infernal Pain,
And fast beside him sat tumultuous Strife:
The one in hand an iron whip did strain,
The other brandished a bloody knife,
And both did gnash their teeth and both did threaten life.[27]

22

On the other side in one consort there sat,
Cruel Revenge, and rancorous° Despite,   *hateful*
Disloyal Treason, and heart-burning Hate,
But gnawing Jealousy out of their sight
Sitting alone, his bitter lips did bite,
And trembling Fear still to and fro did fly,
And found no place, where safe he shroud him might,
Lamenting Sorrow did in darkness lie,
And Shame his ugly face did hide from living eye.[28]

23

And over them sad Horror with grim hue,
Did always sore, beating his iron wings;
And after him owls and night-ravens flew,
The hateful messengers of heavy things,
Of death and dolor° telling sad tidings;   *pain*
Whiles sad Celeno,[29] sitting on a cliff,
A song of bale and bitter sorrow sings,
That heart of flint asunder could have rift°:[30]   *split*
Which having ended, after him she flieth swift.

26. Pluto was the Roman god of the dead and the underworld. So basically this road leads to Hades. This episode places this entire story somewhat in parallel with the great epics of antiquity. Odysseus and Aeneas also visit Hades on their journeys. But ultimately, the archetype of this is found in Jesus who "descended into Hades" for us (see the Apostles' Creed; cf. Eph. 4:8–10, Acts 2:25–31).

27. Pain and Strife are the bouncers at Mammon's party. Looks like a good time.

28. What a bunch of party-poopers. Notice how rotten the whole lot of Mammon's friends are. Sure he can offer you a few riches, but the fine print says you'll spend your days dealing with Revenge, Hatred, Jealousy, Fear, Horror, and all the rest of the gang.

29. She's a harpy: half woman, half bird, a figure associated with avarice and greed.

30. Let's just say she didn't have the best voice. It made strong men cry.

24

All these before the gates of Pluto lay,[31]
By whom they passing, spake unto them naught.
But the Elfin knight with wonder all the way
Did feed his eyes and filled his inner thought.
At last him to a little door he brought,
That to the gate of Hell, which gaped wide,
Was next adjoining, nor them parted ought:
Betwixt them both was but a little stride,
That did the House of Riches from hell-mouth divide.

25

Before the door sat self-consuming Care,
Day and night keeping wary watch and ward°,   *guard*
For fear least Force or Fraud should unaware
Break in, and spoil the treasure there in guard:
Nor would he suffer Sleep once thither-ward
Approach, albe° his drowsy den were next;   *even though*
For next to death is Sleep to be compared:
Therefore his house is unto his annexed°;   *adjoining*
Here Sleep, there Riches, and hell-gate them both betwixt°.   *between*

26

So soon as Mammon there arrived, the door
To him did open, and afforded way;
Him followed eke° Sir Guyon evermore,   *also*
Nor darkness him, nor danger might dismay.
Soon as he entered was, the door straight way
Did shut, and from behind it forth there leapt
An ugly fiend, more foul than dismal day,
The which with monstrous stalk behind him stepped,
And ever as he went, due watch upon him kept.[32]

27

Well hoped he, ere° long that hardy guest,   *before*
If ever covetous hand or lustful eye,
Or lips he laid on thing, that liked him best,
Or ever sleep his eye-strings did untie,

31. The "gates of Pluto" is just the front porch.
32. Now Guyon is really in. And as soon as the door shuts behind him, a fiend begins
to follow him.

Should be his prey.[33] And therefore still on high
He over him did hold his cruel claws,
Threatening with greedy gripe to do him die
And rend in pieces with his ravenous paws,
If ever he transgressed the fatal Stygian[34] laws.

28

That house's form within was rude and strong,
Like an huge cave, hewn out of rocky cliff,
From whose rough vault the ragged breaches° hung,   *stalactites*
Embossed with massy gold of glorious gift,
And with rich metal loaded every rift°,   *crack*
That heavy ruin they did seem to threat;
And over them Arachne high did lift
Her cunning web, and spread her subtle net,
Enwrapped in foul smoke and clouds more black than jet.[35]

29

Both roof and floor and walls were all of gold,
But overgrown with dust and old decay,
And hid in darkness, that none could behold
The hue thereof: for view of cheerful day
Did never in that house itself display,
But a faint shadow of uncertain light;
Such as a lamp, whose life does fade away:
Or as the moon clothed with cloudy night,
Does show to him that walks in fear and sad affright.[36]

30

In all that room was nothing to be seen,
But huge great iron chests and coffers° strong,   *safes*

33. This monstrous beast is tracking Guyon with the hopes of making him supper if he touches something or falls asleep.

34. Stygian means "hellish" or "infernal." It is related to the River Styx which ran through the underworld. The monster also hopes to catch Guyon breaking some rule.

35. You can probably figure out who/what Arachne is. She was a woman in a Greek myth who lost a weaving contest with Athena, so she was turned into a spider. Moral of the story: never compete with the gods. Whether you win or lose, they'll find some reason to turn you into something unpleasant, like a McDonald's Happy Meal. And there's nothing "happy" about that.

36. The walls and floor are all of gold, but they are covered with dirt, dust, and grime, and the sun doesn't shine there anyway. The place is loaded with riches, but notice how they are completely unused and never enjoyed.

All bared with double bends that none could ween°   *think*
Them to efforce° by violence or wrong;   *break open*
On every side they placed were along.
But all the ground with skulls was scattered,
And dead men's bones, which round about were flung,
Whose lives, it seemed, whilome° there were shed,   *formerly*
And their vile carcasses now left unburied.

31

They forward pass, nor Guyon yet spoke word,
Till that they came unto an iron door,
Which to them opened of his own accord,
And showed of riches such exceeding store,
As eye of man did never see before;
Nor ever could within one place be found,
Though all the wealth, which is, or was of yore,
Could gathered be through all the world around,
And that above were added to that under ground.

32

The charge thereof unto a covetous sprite°   *spirit*
Commanded was, who thereby did attend,
And warily awaited day and night,
From other covetous fiends it to defend,
Who it to rob and ransack did intend.
Then Mammon turning to that warrior, said;
"Lo here the world's bliss, lo here the end,
To which all men do aim, rich to be made:
Such grace now to be happy, is before thee laid."[37]

33

"Certes°," said he, "I no ill thine offered grace,   *certainly*
Nor to be made so happy do intend:
Another bliss before mine eyes I place,
Another happiness, another end.[38]
To them, that list°, these base regards I lend: *want*

37. I.e., "This is it, Guyon, this is everything anyone could ever want." Mammon is a false god offering a false "grace."

38. I.e., "Surely I don't mean ill to your offered grace, nor do I not want to be happy, but I'm in search of another happiness." Often this is thrown in the face of Christians: "Don't you want to have fun?" And we must learn to answer the challenge like Guyon. We want happiness, but we want a fuller and richer happiness. Go Guyon.

But I in arms, and in achievements brave,
Do rather choose my flitting hours to spend,
And to be lord of those that riches have,
Than them to have myself and be their servile slave."

34

Thereat the fiend his gnashing teeth did grate,
And grieved so long to lack his greedy prey;
For well he weened°, that so glorious bait   *thought*
Would tempt his guest, to take thereof assay°:   *test*
Had he so done, he had him snatched away,
More light than culver° in the Falcon's fist.[39]   *dove, pigeon*
Eternal God thee save from such decay.
But when as Mammon saw his purpose missed,
Him to entrap unawares another way he wist°.[40]   *thought*

35

Thence forward he him led and shortly brought
Unto another room, whose door forthright,
To him did open, as it had been taught:
Therein an hundred ranges° were pight°,   *ovens / placed*
And hundred furnaces all burning bright;
By every furnace many fiends did bide,
Deformed creatures, horrible in sight,
And every fiend his busy pains applied,
To melt the golden metal, ready to be tried.

36

One with great bellows gathered filling air,
And with forced wind the fuel did inflame;
Another did the dying brands repair
With iron tongs and sprinkled oft the same
With liquid waves, fierce Vulcan's[41] rage to tame,
Who mastering them, renewed his former heat;
Some scummed° the dross that from the metal came;   *skimmed*
Some stirred the molten ore with ladles great;
And everyone did swink° and everyone did sweat.   *work*

39. If Guyon had taken the riches, he would have been dead in a moment.
40. Mammon is pretty upset that Guyon didn't give in, but he won't give up so easily.
41. Remember, he's the Roman god of fire and metalworking.

37

But when as earthly wight° they present saw,	*creature*

But when as earthly wight° they present saw,   *creature*
Glistering in arms and battelous array,
From their hot work they did themselves withdraw
To wonder at the sight: for till that day,
They never creature saw, that came that way.
Their staring eyes sparkling with fervent fire,
And ugly shapes did nigh the man dismay,
That were it not for shame, he would retire,
Till that him thus bespake their sovereign lord and sire.

38

"Behold, thou faerie's son, with mortal eye,
That living eye before did never see:
The thing, that thou didst crave so earnestly,
To weet°, whence all the wealth late showed by me,   *think*
Proceeded, lo now is revealed to thee.
Here is the fountain of the world's good:
Now therefore, if thou wilt enrichéd be,
Advise thee well, and change thy willful mood,
Lest thou perhaps hereafter wish, and be withstood."[42]

39

"Suffice it then, thou money god," quoth he,
"That all thine idle offers I refuse.[43]
All that I need I have; what needeth me
To covet more than I have cause to use?
With such vain shows thy worldlings vile abuse:
But give me leave to follow mine emprise°.   *mission*
Mammon was much displeased, yet no'te° he choose,   *could not*
But bear the rigor of his bold misprise°,   *contempt*
And thence him forward led, him further to entice.[44]

40

He brought him through a dark-some narrow strait,
To a broad gate, all built of beaten gold:

42. Mammon tries again, this time offering not just a mountain of money, but the very furnaces that create the precious metals of the world.

43. Notice that these temptations are similar to the temptation of Christ in the wilderness by the Devil (Mt. 4:1–11, Lk. 4:1–12).

44. Mammon stubbornly seeks to hook Guyon.

The gate was open, but therein did wait
A sturdy villain, striding stiff and bold,
As if that highest God defy he would;
In his right hand an iron club he held,
But he himself was all of golden mold,
Yet had both life and sense and well could wield
That curséd weapon, when his cruel foes he quelled.

41

Disdain he calléd was, and did disdain
To be so called, and who so did him call:
Stern was his look, and full of stomach° vain,   *anger*
His portance terrible, and stature tall,
Far passing the height of men terrestrial°;   *earthly*
Like an huge giant of the Titan's[45] race,
That made him scorn all creatures great and small,
And with his pride all others' power deface:
More fit amongst black fiends, than men to have his place.

42

Soon as those glitter and arms he did espy°,   *see*
That with their brightness made that darkness light,
His harmful club he 'gan to hurtle high,
And threaten battle to the faerie knight;
Who likewise 'gan himself to battle dight°,   *prepare*
Till Mammon did his hasty hand withhold,
And counseled him abstain from perilous fight:
For nothing might abash the villain bold,
Nor mortal steel empierce his miscreated° mould.[46]   *deformed*

43

So having him with reason pacified,
And the fierce carl° commanding to forbear,   *villain*
He brought him in. The room was large and wide,
As it some guild or solemn temple were:
Many great golden pillars did up bear
The massy° roof, and riches huge sustain,   *massive*

45. The Titans were a race of Greek gods.
46. As Mammon continues the tour, they meet Disdain, who's guarding a large door-way. He's a giant, ugly man with a bad attitude. They prepare to fight each other, but Mammon counsels Guyon not to fight because Disdain happens to be invincible to "mortal steel."

And every pillar decked was full dear
With crowns and diadems and titles vain,
Which mortal princes wore, whiles they on earth did reign.

44

A rout° of people there assembled were,   *riotous crowd*
Of every sort and nation under sky,
Which with great uproar pressed to draw near
To the upper part, where was advanced high
A stately siege of sovereign majesty;
And thereon sat a woman gorgeous gay,
And richly clad in robes of royalty,
That never earthly prince in such array
His glory did enhance and pompous pride display.[47]

45

Her face right wondrous fair did seem to be,
That her broad beauty's beam great brightness threw
Through the dim shade, that all men might it see:
Yet was not that same her own native hue,
But wrought by art and counterfeited show,
Thereby more lovers unto her to call;
Natheless° most heavenly fair in deed and view   *nevertheless*
She by creation was, till she did fall;
Thenceforth she sought for helps, to cloak her crime withal.[48]

46

There, as in glistering glory she did sit,
She held a great gold chain ylinked° well,   *constructed*
Whose upper end to highest heaven was knit,
And lower part did reach to lowest Hell;
And all that press did round about her swell,
To catch hold of that long chain, thereby
To clime aloft and others to excel:
That was Ambition, rash desire to sty°,   *climb*
And every link thereof a step of dignity.[49]

47. Mammon leads Guyon into the room which turns out to be a vaulted room full of people crowding around a stage upon which sat a woman decked in royal clothes. She looks like a queen.

48. This beautiful woman had been beautiful naturally but had "fallen," and since then it took art and trickery to make her look so well (i.e., lots of makeup).

49. The chain's name is Ambition.

47

Some thought to raise themselves to high degree,
By riches and unrighteous reward,
Some by close shouldering, some by flattery;
Others through friends, others for base regard;
And all by wrong ways for themselves prepared.
Those that were up themselves, kept others low,
Those that were low themselves, held others hard,
Nor suffered them to rise or greater grow,
But every one did strive his fellow down to throw.[50]

48

Which when as Guyon saw, he 'gan inquire,
What meant that press about that lady's throne,
And what she was that did so high aspire.
Him Mammon answered: "That goodly one,
Whom all that folk with such contention,
Do flock about, my dear my daughter is;
Honor and dignity from her alone,
Derivéd are, and all this world's bliss
For which ye men do strive: few get, but many miss.

49

"And fair Philotime she rightly hight°,   *called*
The fairest wight° that wonneth° under sky,   *creature / lives*
But that this dark-some nether world her light
Doth dim with horror and deformity,
Worthy of heaven and high felicity,
From whence the gods have her for envy thrust:
But since thou hast found favor in mine eye,
Thy spouse I will her make, if that thou lust,[51]
That she may thee advance for works and merits just."

50

"Gramercy[52] Mammon," said the gentle knight,
"For so great grace and offered high estate;

50. Of course Jesus said that the one who would be the greatest in the Kingdom must become the servant of all, and it is the humble who will be exalted. Those who exalt themselves will be humbled. The first shall be last, and the last shall be first. He who wants to find his life must lose it. This crowd does the exact opposite, but hey, what'd you expect?

51. I.e., "I'll make her your wife if you want."

52. I.e., [surprise and gratitude] "Wow, thanks!"

But I, that am frail flesh and earthly wight°,   *creature*
Unworthy match for such immortal mate
Myself well wote°, and mine unequal fate;   *know*
And were I not, yet is my troth yplight°,   *pledged*
And love avowed to other lady late,[53]
That to remove the same I have no might:
To change love causeless is reproach to warlike knight."

51

Mammon emmovéd was with inward wrath;
Yet forcing it to feign, him forth thence led
Through grisly shadows by a beaten path,
Into a garden goodly garnished
With herbs and fruits, whose kinds mote° not be read°:   *might / known*
Not such, as earth out of her fruitful womb
Throws forth to men, sweet and well savored,
But direful deadly black both leaf and bloom,
Fit to adorn the dead, and deck the dreary tomb.[54]

52

There mournful cypress grew in greatest store,
And trees of bitter gall, and ebon° sad,   *ebony, black*
Dead sleeping poppy and black hellebore,[55]
Cold coloquintida and tetra[56] mad,
Mortal samnitis and cicuta[57] bad,
With which the unjust Athenians made to die
Wise Socrates, who thereof quaffing° glad   *drinking*
Poured out his life, and last philosophy
To the fair Critias[58] his dearest belamy°.   *friend*

53. I.e., "I'm already betrothed to another woman."

54. Mammon's last attempt at wooing Guyon was with his daughter, Philotime. But after Guyon turns this last offer down, Mammon leads Guyon out of the underworld. They come into a garden which is unlike any garden on earth. It is full of black plants. The leaves, flowers, and blooms of everything in the garden are completely black: The garden of the dead, the Garden of Proserpina.

55. A poisonous Eurasian plant.

56. Both of these are other deadly plants.

57. And that's hemlock.

58. Apparently this Critias fellow wasn't as tight with Socrates as Spenser thought. All the commentaries say so. They base this on Plato's *Phaedo*. Go figure.

53

The Garden of Proserpina this hight°;   *called*
And in the midst thereof a silver seat,
With a thick arbor goodly over dight°,   *covered*
In which she often used from open heat
Herself to shroud and pleasures to entreat.
Next thereunto did grow a goodly tree,
With branches broad dispread and body great,
Clothed with leaves, that none the wood mote° see   *might*
And laden all with fruit as thick as it might be.

54

Their fruit were golden apples glistering bright,
That goodly was their glory to behold,
On earth like never grew, nor living wight°   *creature*
Like ever saw, but° they from hence were sold;[59]   *unless*
For those, which Hercules with conquest bold
Got from great Atlas' daughters, hence began,
And planted there, did bring forth fruit of gold:
And those with which the Eubaean young man wan°   *won*
Swift Atalanta, when through craft he her out ran.

55

Here also sprung that goodly golden fruit,
With which Acontius got his lover true,
Whom he had long time sought with fruitless suit°:   *pursuit*
Here eke° that famous golden apple grew,   *also*
The which amongst the gods false Ate[60] threw;
For which the Idaean Ladies disagreed,
Till partial Paris deemed it Venus due,
And had of her, fair Helen for his meed°,   *reward*
That many noble Greeks and Trojans made to bleed.[61]

59. So in the middle of the garden is this big, black tree. And on this tree are tons of golden apples. Everything is black except the apples. The apples are golden. Kind of eerie.

60. That's the goddess of discord, of course.

61. That's the origin of the Trojan War in a nutshell. The goddess of discord tossed an apple with the inscription "to the fairest" into the midst of three goddesses. After some bargaining Paris chose Venus (who the Greeks called Aphrodite) as the fairest, and in exchange he was awarded Helen, the most beautiful woman in the world. And thus began the Trojan War. More on this later.

56

The warlike elf[62] much wondered at this tree,
So fair and great, that shadowed all the ground,
And his broad branches, laden with rich fee,
Did stretch themselves without the utmost bound
Of this great garden, compassed with a mound,
Which over-hanging, they themselves did steep,
In a black flood which flowed about it round;
That is the river of Cocytus[63] deep,
In which full many souls do endless wail and weep.

57

Which to behold, he climbed up to the bank,
And looking down, saw many damnéd wights°,   *creatures*
In those sad waves, which direful deadly stank,
Plunged continually of cruél sprites°,   *spirits*
That with their piteous cries, and yelling shrights°,   *shrieks*
They made the further shore resound° wide: *echo*
Amongst the rest of those same rueful° sights,   *pitiful*
One curséd creature, he by chance espied,
That drenchéd lay full deep, under the garden side.[64]

58

Deep was he drenched to the up most chin,
Yet gaped still, as coveting to drink
Of the cold liquor, which he waded in,
And stretching forth his hand, did often think
To reach the fruit, which grew upon the brink:
But both the fruit from hand, and flood from mouth
Did fly aback, and made him vainly swink°:   *work*
The whiles he starved with hunger and with drought
He daily died, yet never thoroughly die couth°.[65]   *could*

62. That's Guyon.
63. A river in Hades.
64. Guyon notices that the garden is on the banks of a river (the Cocytus). So he goes over to take a look and sees lots of dead folks in the river yelling and screaming. This short scene pictures some of the infamous wicked judged for their sins. These characters also appear in other Classical and Medieval literature. Spenser uses these well-known characters for his own purposes of showing temperance and intemperance.
65. Though he starved and thirsted to death each day, he could never really die.

59

The knight him seeing labor so in vain,
Asked who he was, and what he meant thereby:
Who groaning deep, thus answered him again;
"Most curséd of all creatures under sky,
Lo Tantalus, I here tormented lie:
Of whom high Jove want whylome° feasted be,   *used to*
Lo here I now for want of food do die:
But if that thou be such, as I thee see,
Of grace I pray thee, give to eat and drink to me."[66]

60

"Nay, nay, thou greedy Tantalus," quoth he,
"Abide the fortune of thy present fate,
And unto all that live in high degree,
Ensample° be of mind intemperate,   *example*
To teach them how to use their present state."[67]
Then 'gan the curséd wretch aloud to cry,
Accusing highest Jove and gods ingrate,
And eke° blaspheming heaven bitterly,   *also*
As author of unjustice, there to let him die.

61

He looked a little further, and espied
Another wretch, whose carcass deep was drowned[68]
Within the river, which the same did hide:
But both his hands most filthy feculent°,   *covered in feces*
Above the water were on high extent,
And feigned° to wash themselves incessantly;   *tried*
Yet nothing cleaner were for such intent,
But rather fouler seemed to the eye;
So lost his labor vain and idle industry.

66. Tantalus is a character forever remembered as synonymous with greed. He either served his own son for a meal to the gods or tried to trick them in some other way. Here, Tantalus refers to Jove as the god who was offended in particular, and as a punishment he was forever buried to the neck, hungry and thirsty with an apple just out of reach. Tantalus asks Guyon for a drink of water.

67. Guyon refuses to give Tantalus a drink because Tantalus is an example of intemperance to all who pass by.

68. He's not really drowned, but his body is deep in the water.

62

The knight him calling, asked who he was,
Who lifting up his head, him answered thus:
"I Pilate am the falsest judge, alas,
And most unjust, that by unrighteous
And wicked doom, to Jews dispiteous°   *pitiless*
Delivered up the Lord of life to die,
And did acquit a murderer felonious;
The whiles my hands I washed in purity,
The whiles my soul was soiled with foul iniquity."[69]

63

Infinite more, tormented in like pain
He there beheld, too long here to be told:
Nor Mammon would there let him long remain,
For terror of the tortures manifold,
In which the damnéd souls he did behold,
But roughly him bespake. "Thou fearful fool,
Why takest not of that same fruit of gold,
Nor sittest down on that same silver stool,
To rest thy weary person, in the shadow cool."

64

All which he did, to do him deadly fall
In frail intemperance through sinful bait;
To which if he inclined had at all,
That dreadful fiend, which did behind him wait,
Would him have rent in thousand pieces strait:[70]
But he was wary° wise in all his way,   *careful*
And well perceived his deceitful sleight°,   *trick*
Nor suffered lust his safety to betray;
So goodly did beguile the guiler° of the prey.   *deceiver*

65

And now he has so long remainéd there,
That vital powers 'gan wax both weak and wan°,   *pale*
For want of food, and sleep, which two up bear°,   *support*

69. The next person Guyon sees is Pontius Pilate, the Roman governor who ordered the crucifixion of Jesus.

70. Mammon encourages Guyon to take an apple and sit down and rest for a bit. But if Sir Guyon had tried to take a snack or a short snooze, he'd be done for. Remember the monster?

Like mighty pillars, this frail life of man,
That none without the same endure can.
For now three days of men were full out wrought,
Since he this hardy enterprise began:
For thy great Mammon fairly he besought,
Into the world to guide him back, as he him brought.

66

The god, though loath°, yet was constrained to obey,	*unwilling*
For longer time, than that, no living wight°	*creature*
Below the earth, might suffered be to stay:[71]	
So back again, him brought to living light.	
But all so soon as his enfeebled spright°	*spirit*
'Gan suck this vital air into his breast,	
As overcome with too exceeding might,	
The life did flit away out of her nest,	
And all his senses were with deadly fit oppressed.[72]	

71. No living creature can be kept below the earth for more than three days . . . hmmm. Remind you of anyone else?

72. Uh-oh. Sir Guyon faints. Although Guyon endured a temptation much like Christ's, Spenser makes it clear that Guyon needs a savior, a defender from his enemies.

Can You Dig It?

Directions: Identify where in the story the following quotes came from. Explain what they mean and their significance to the story.

1. "Do not I kings create, and throw the crown
    Sometimes to him, that low in dust doth lie?
    And him that reigned, into his room thrust down,
    And whom I lust do heap with glory and renown?"

2. "And were I not, yet is my troth yplight,
    And love avowed to other lady late,
    That to remove the same I have no might:
    To change love causeless is reproach to warlike knight."

3. "But he was wary wise in all his way,
    And well perceived his deceitful sleight,
    Nor suffered lust his safety to betray;
    So goodly did beguile the guiler of the prey."

Canto VIII.

Sir Guyon laid in swoon is by
Acrates' sons despoiled,
Whom Arthur soon hath rescuéd
And Paynim° brethren foiled.   *Pagan*

1

And is there care in heaven? And is there love
In heavenly spirits to these creatures base,
That may compassion of their evils move?
There is: else much more wretched were the case
Of men, than beasts.[1] But O the exceeding grace
Of highest God, that loves his creatures so,
And all his works with mercy doth embrace,
That blessed angels, he sends to and fro,
To serve to wicked man, to serve his wicked foe.

2

How oft do they, their silver bowers leave,
To come to succor us that succor want?[2]
How oft do they with golden pinions°, cleave   *wings*
The flitting skies, like flying pursuant°,   *prosecutor*
Against foul fiends to aid us militant?

1. Spenser says that one of the ways in which our condition as people is better off than animals is that there is a special care in heaven for us.
2. I.e., to help those who need help.

They for us fight, they watch and duly ward,
And their bright squadrons round about us plant,
And all for love, and nothing for reward:
O why should heavenly God to man have such regard?

3

During the while, that Guyon did abide
In Mammon's house, the Palmer, whom whyleare°   *earlier*
That wanton maid³ of passage had denied,
By further search had passage found elsewhere,
And being on his way, approachéd near,
Where Guyon lay in trance, when suddenly
He heard a voice, that calléd loud and clear,
"Come hither, come hither, O come hastily";
That all the fields resounded with the rueful° cry.⁴   *sorrowful*

4

The Palmer lent his ear unto the noise,
To weet°, who called so importunely°:   *know / urgently*
Again he heard a more efforcéd° voice,   *forceful*
That bade him come in haste. He by and by
His feeble feet directed to the cry;
Which to that shady delve him brought at last,
Where Mammon earst° did sun his treasury: *before*
There the good Guyon he found slumbering fast
In senseless dream; which sight at first him sore aghast.

5

Beside his head there sat a fair young man,
Of wondrous beauty, and of freshest years,
Whose tender bud to blossom new began,
And flourish fair above his equal peers;
His snowy front curléd with golden hairs,
Like Phoebus' face° adorned with sunny rays,   *the sun*
Divinely shone, and two sharp winged shears°,   *blades*
Decked with diverse° plumes, like painted jays,   *different colored*
Were fixed at his back, to cut his aerie° ways.⁵   *heavenly*

3. Remember that was Phaedria, the flower child.
4. The Palmer finally finds another passage over the stream, and while searching for Guyon, he hears an urgent voice calling him to come quickly.
5. He follows the shouts until he comes to the entrance of Mammon's cave where Guyon is lying with an angel-child sitting beside him.

6

Like as Cupido on Idaean hill,
When having laid his cruél bow away,
And mortal arrows, wherewith he doth fill
The world with murderous spoils and bloody prey,[6]
With his fair mother° he him dights° to play,   *Aphrodite / clothes*
And with his goodly sisters, Graces three;
The goddess pleaséd with his wanton play,
Suffers herself through sleep beguiléd to be,
The whiles the other ladies mind their merry glee.[7]

7

Whom when the Palmer saw, abashed he was
Through fear and wonder, that he naught could say,
Till him the child bespoke, "Long lacked, alas,
Hath been thy faithful aid in hard assay°,   *trial*
Whiles deadly fit thy pupil doth dismay;
Behold this heavy sight, thou reverend sire,
But dread of death and dolor° do away;   *pain*
For life ere° long shall to her home retire,   *before*
And he that breathless seems, shall courage bold respire°.[8]   *enliven*

8

"The charge, which God doth unto me aret°,   *entrust*
Of his dear safety, I to thee commend;
Yet will I not forgo, nor yet forget

6. The "Idaean hill" is Mount Ida, where Paris judged between Hera, Athena, and Aphrodite, as to which was the most beautiful. Each of the goddesses attempted to bribe Paris, and Aphrodite won by promising to provide Paris with the most beautiful woman in the world (Helen). Cupid was often pictured in Renaissance artwork as a child with wings and the deceiver of Paris, causing him to go for the girl. This is why Spenser describes Cupid filling the world with "murderous spoils and bloody prey."

7. The Three Graces were supposed to be daughters of Zeus, their names being Aglaia (Splendor), Euphrosyne (Mirth), and Thalia (Good Cheer). This whole stanza is a description of the angel caring for Guyon. It seems that Spenser's point is simply a physical description. Spenser is describing a particular piece of art or a conglomeration of depictions of this scene. There are a number of Renaissance paintings that are titled "The Judgment of Paris" which broadly fit Spenser's description here. The angel guarding Guyon is like Cupid, a winged child. This is one unfortunate aspect of much Renaissance art (and consequently Spenser's angelic depiction). That period gave us naked, winged babies and has kept Hallmark and other sappy Christian gift shops in business for far too long.

8. I.e., "You've been missed, but don't worry, Guyon will be all right."

The care thereof myself unto the end,[9]
But evermore him succor°, and defend   *aid*
Against his foe and mine: watch thou I pray;
For evil is at hand him to offend."
So having said, eftsoones° he 'gan display   *presently*
His painted nimble wings, and vanished quite away.

9

The Palmer seeing his left empty place,
And his slow eyes beguiled of their sight,
Wax sore afraid, and standing still a space,
Gazed after him, as fowl escaped by flight;
At last him turning to his charge behight°,   *entrusted*
With trembling hand his troubled pulse 'gan try;
Where finding life not yet dislodgéd quite,
He much rejoiced, and cured it tenderly,
As chicken newly hatched, from dreaded destiny.[10]

10

At last he spied, where towards him did pace
Two paynim° knights, all armed as bright as sky,   *pagan*
And them beside an agéd sire did trace,
And far before a light-foot page did fly,
That breathed strife and troublous enmity;[11]
Those were the two sons of Acrates old
Who meeting earst with Archimago sly,
Foreby that idle strand° of him were told,   *beach*
That he, which earst° them combated, was Guyon bold.   *formerly*

11

Which to avenge on him they dearly vowed,
Where ever that on ground they mote° him find;   *might*
False Archimage provoked their courage proud,
And strife-full Atin in their stubborn mind

9. He hands Guyon back over to the Palmer but promises to see Guyon's mission to its end.

10. The angel suddenly flies away, and this scares the Palmer. But he recovers after a few moments, checks Guyon's pulse, and finding him still alive, begins caring for Guyon.

11. Guess who?

Coals of contention and hot vengeance tined.[12]
Now been they come whereas the Palmer sat,
Keeping° that slumbered corpse to him assigned;   *guarding*
Well knew they both his person, since of late
With him in bloody arms they rashly did debate.[13]

12

Whom when Pyrochles saw, inflamed with rage,
That sire he foul bespake, "Thou dotard° vile,   *old fool*
That with thy bruteness shendst° thy comely age,   *shames*
Abandon soon, I read°, the caitiff° spoil   *say / cowardly*
Of that same outcast carcass that ere-while°   *a little while ago*
Made itself famous through false treachery,
And crowned his coward crest with knightly style;
Lo where he now inglorious doth lie,
To prove he lived ill, that did thus foully die."[14]

13

To whom the Palmer fearless answered;
"Certes°, sir knight, ye been too much to blame,   *truly*
Thus for to blot the honor of the dead,
And with foul cowardice his carcass shame,
Whose living hands immortalized his name.[15]
Vile is the vengeance on the ashes cold,
And envy base, to bark at sleeping fame:
Was never wight°, that treason of him told;   *creature*
Yourself his prowess proved and found him fierce and bold."

14

Then said Cymochles: "Palmer, thou doest dote°,   *speak foolishly*
Nor canst of prowess, nor of knighthood deem°,   *judge*
Save as thou seest or hearst. But well I wote°,   *know*
That of his puissance° trial made extreme;   *strength*
Yet gold all is not, that doth golden seem,
Nor all good knights, that shake well spear and shield:

12. A tine is something pointy like antlers or a pitchfork. Atin prods Pyrochles and
Cymochles with hot vengeance. And Archimago adds his two cents too.

13. The brothers recognize their foe immediately.

14. Did you catch Pyrochles' accusation? He claims that Guyon's foul "death" proves
he was a coward and not worthy of the title of knighthood. I wonder if these guys know
any of Job's friends.

15. The name Guyon means something like "lively struggle."

The worth of all men by their end esteem,
And then due praise, or due reproach them yield;
Bad therefore I him deem, that thus lies dead on field.[16]

15

"Good or bad," 'gan his brother fierce reply,
"What do I reck°, since that he died entire?   *think*
Or what doth his bad death now satisfy
The greedy hunger of revenging ire°,   *wrath*
Since wrathful hand wrought not her own desire?
Yet since no way is left to wreak my spite,
I will him reave° of arms, the victor's hire,   *strip*
And of that shield, more worthy of good knight;
For why should a dead dog be decked in armor bright?"[17]

16

"Fair sir," said then the Palmer suppliant°,   *beseeching*
"For knighthood's love, do not so foul a deed,
Nor blame your honor with so shameful vaunt
Of vile revenge. To spoil the dead of weed°   *armor*
Is sacrilege, and doth all sins exceed;
But leave these relics of his living might,
To deck his hearse,[18] and trap his tomb-black steed.
What hearse or steed," said he, "should he have dight°,   *cover*
But° be entombed in the raven or the kite?"[19]   *except*

17

With that, rude hand upon his shield he laid,
And the other brother 'gan his helm unlace,[20]
Both fiercely bent to have him disarrayed;
Till that they spied, where towards them did pace

16. I.e., "You can't judge everybody by their fighting abilities. I judge men by how they turn out. He's dead, therefore he was a coward." Cymochles agrees with this brother's earlier assessment.

17. Pyrochles proposes to strip the armor off Guyon.

18. A "hearse" is that funny looking car that carries a casket. Of course this would have referred to whatever carried Guyon to his final rest. Notice however that Palmer is going along with the brothers' assessment. He knows Guyon isn't really dead. He's buying time.

19. I.e., "If you take his armor, he'll end up buried in the belly of a bird."

20. The Palmer's brave protests are completely ignored by the two brothers and they start pulling Guyon's armor off.

An arméd knight, of bold and bounteous grace,
Whose squire bore after him an ebon° lance,   *ebony, black*
And covered shield. Well kenned° him so far space   *knew*
The enchanter by his arms and immanence°,   *majesty*
When under him he saw his Lybian steed to prance.[21]

18

And to those brethren said, "Rise, rise by live°,   *immediately*
And unto battle do yourselves address;
For yonder comes the prowest° knight alive,   *fiercest*
Prince Arthur, flower of grace and nobiless,[22]
That hath to paynim° knights wrought great distress,   *pagan*
And thousand Sar'cens° foully done to die."   *Saracens, Muslims*
That word so deep did in their hearts impress,
That both eftsoones° up started furiously,   *right away*
And 'gan themselves prepare to battle greedily.

19

But fierce Pyrochles, lacking his own sword,
The want° thereof now greatly 'gan to plain°,   *need / complain*
And Archimage besought, him that afford,
Which he had brought for Braggadocchio vain.
"So would I," said the enchanter, "glad and feign
Beteem° to you this sword, you to defend,   *give*
Or ought that else your honor might maintain,
But that this weapon's power I well have kenned°,   *known*
To be contrary to the work, which ye intend.

20

"For that same knight's own sword this is of yore,
Which Merlin made by his almighty art
For that his nursling, when he knighthood swore,
Therewith to done his foes eternal smart°.   *hurt*
The metal first he mixed with medaewart,[23]
That no enchantment from his dint might save;
That it in flames of Aetna[24] wrought apart,

21. The enchanter is Archimago. He recognizes the knight who is riding towards them by his nobility, arms, and the horse he rode. Who is it?

22. That's nobility of course; it's Arthur, ain't it?

23. This is Meadowsweet, an herb with medicinal qualities.

24. Aetna is related to Vulcan's fire (he's the god of fire), where various weapons and swords were forged.

And seven times dipped in the bitter wave
Of hellish Styx, which hidden virtue to it gave.

21

"The virtue is that neither steel nor stone
The stroke thereof from entrance may defend;
Nor ever may be used by his foe,
Nor forced his rightful owner to offend,
Nor ever will it break, nor ever bend.
Wherefore Mordure²⁵ it rightfully is hight°.   *named*
In vain therefore, Pyrochles, should I lend
The same to thee, against his lord to fight,
For sure it would deceive thy labor and thy might."²⁶

22

"Foolish old man," said then the pagan wroth°,   *angrily*
"That weenest²⁷ words or charms may force withstand:
Soon shalt thou see, and then believe for troth°,   *truth*
That I can carve with this enchanted brand
His Lord's own flesh." Therewith out of his hand
That virtuous steel he rudely snatched away,
And Guyon's shield about his wrist he bound;
So ready dight°, fierce battle to assay°,   *clad / test*
And match his brother proud in battelous array.²⁸

23

By this that stranger knight in presence came,
And goodly saluted them; who naught again
Him answered, as courtesy became,
But with stern looks, and stomachous²⁹ disdain,
Gave signs of grudge and discontentment vain:
Then turning to the Palmer, he 'gan spy

---

25. Mordure means "bite cruelly."

26. Pyrochles doesn't have a sword and he immediately asks Archimago for the sword he has. Remember, Archimago had gone to get Arthur's sword for Braggadochio. Archimago explains to Pyrochles that this sword was fashioned with hidden virtue so that it cannot hurt its rightful owner (Arthur).

27. I.e., "He that thinks . . ."

28. Pyrochles mocks Archimago, takes the sword and Guyon's shield, and joins his brother preparing to fight Arthur.

29. What a good word—think of the bile and acid in the stomach.

Where at his feet, with sorrowful demean°   *look*
And deadly hue, an arméd corpse did lie,
In whose dead face he read great magnanimity.[30]

24

Said he then to the Palmer, "Reverend sire,
What great misfortune hath betide this knight?
Or did his life her fatal date expire,
Or did he fall by treason, or by fight?
How ever, sure I rue° his piteous plight."   *feel sorry for*
"Not one, nor other," said the Palmer grave,
"Hath him befallen, but clouds of deadly night
A while his heavy eyelids covered have,
And all his senses drownéd in deep senseless wave.

25

"Which, those his cruél foes, that stand hereby,
Making advantage, to revenge their spite,
Would him disarm and treat shamefully,
Unworthy usage of redoubted knight.
But you, fair sir, whose honorable sight
Doth promise hope of help and timely grace,
Mote° I beseech to succor° his sad plight,   *might / help*
And by your power protect his feeble case.
First praise of knighthood is foul outrage to deface."[31]

26

"Palmer," said he, "no knight so rude, I ween°,   *know*
As to do outrage to a sleeping ghost:
Nor was there ever noble courage seen,
That in advantage would his puissance° boast: *strength*
Honor is least where odds appeareth most.
Maybe, that better reason will assuage
The rash revenger's heat. Words well disposed
Have secret power, to appease inflaméd rage:
If not, leave unto me thy knight's last patronage."[32]

30. Arthur sees greatness in the face of Guyon.
31. The Palmer explains that Guyon has passed out and that the two sons of Acrates are trying to strip his armor. He asks Arthur to protect Guyon.
32. Arthur says that sometimes talking and explaining a situation is the best way to deal with rage.

27

Though turning to those brethren, thus bespoke,
"Ye warlike pair, whose valorous great might
It seems, just wrongs to vengeance do provoke,
To wreak your wrath on this dead seeming knight,
Mote° ought allay° the storm of your despite,   *might / relieve*
And settle patience in so furious heat?[33]
Not to debate the challenge of your right,
But for this carcass pardon I entreat,
Whom fortune hath already laid in lowest seat."[34]

28

To whom Cymochles said, "For what art thou,
That makest thyself his days-man°, to prolong   *lawyer*
The vengeance pressed? Or who shall let° me now,   *stop*
On this vile body from to wreak my wrong,
And make his carcass as the outcast dung?
Why should not that dead carrion satisfy
The guilt, which if he livéd had thus long,
His life for due revenge should dear abie°?   *abide*
The trespass still doth live, albe° the person die."[35]   *even if*

29

"Indeed," then said the Prince, "the evil done
Dies not, when breath the body first doth leave,
But from the grandsire to the nephew's son,
And all his seed the curse doth often cleave,
Till vengeance utterly the guilt bereave:
So straightly God doth judge. But gentle knight,
That doth against the dead his hand up rear,
His honor stains with rancor° and despite,   *malice*
And great disparagement makes to his former might."[36]

33. I.e., "Might something else relieve your anger?"

34. I.e., "Come on guys, can't you find someone else to pick on? This guy is already laid pretty low."

35. Cymochles says that wrongdoing does not just go away when someone dies.

36. Arthur agrees with Cymochles, but he says that God judges the actions of men and that Cymochles would disgrace the honor of Guyon's good qualities by stripping his armor.

30

Pyrochles 'gan reply the second time,
And to him said, "Now felon sure I read°,   *see*
How that thou art partaker of his crime:
Therefore by Termagaunt[37] thou shalt be dead."[38]
With that his hand, more sad than lump of lead,
Uplifting high, he weened° with Mordure,   *thought*
His own good sword Mordure, to cleave his head.
The faithful steel such treason no'uld° endure,   *nothing could*
But swerving from the mark, his lord's life did assure.[39]

31

Yet was the force so furious and so fell,
That horse and man it made to reel aside;
Natheless° the Prince[40] would not forsake his sell°:   *nevertheless / saddle*
For well of yore he learnéd had to ride,[41]
But full of anger fiercely to him cried;
"False traitor miscreant, thou broken hast
The law of arms, to strike foe undefied.
But thou thy treason's fruit, I hope, shalt taste
Right sore and feel the law, the which thou hast defaced."

32

With that his baleful spear, he fiercely bent
Against the pagan's breast and therewith thought
His curséd life out of her lodge have rent:
But ere° the point arrivéd, where it ought,   *before*
That seven-fold shield, which he from Guyon brought
He cast between to ward the bitter stound°:   *blow*
Through all those folds the steelhead passage wrought

37. This fellow was a deity with unknown associations with Islam.
38. Pyrochles, never a man for words, decides that Arthur is "in" on Guyon's treason, whatever that may be . . . and threatens to kill Arthur.
39. Pyrochles lifts Arthur's sword and takes a swing at Arthur, but the sword refuses to hurt its owner and swerves to miss Arthur's head. That's a trusty sword: safe even in the hands of an enemy.
40. The "Prince" is Arthur. Spenser commonly uses this as an alternate title for Arthur.
41. Remember our friend Braggadochio, the horse rustler? Spenser mocked him for not being able to ride, but Arthur is as good as they come.

And through his shoulder pierced; wherewith to ground
He groveling fell, all gored in his gushing wound.[42]

33

Which when his brother saw, fraught with great grief
And wrath, he to him leaped furiously,
And foully said, "By Mahoune,[43] cursèd thief,
That direful stroke thou dearly shalt buy."[44]
Then hurling up his harmful blade on high,
Smote him so hugely on his haughty crest,
That from his saddle forced him to fly:
Else mote it needs down to his manly breast
Have cleft his head in twain, and life thence dispossessed.[45]

34

Now was the Prince in dangerous distress,
Wanting his sword, when he on foot should fight:
His single spear could do him small redress,
Against two foes of so exceeding might,
The least of which was match for any knight.[46]
And now the other, whom he earst° did daunt,   *first*
Had reared himself again to cruel fight,
Three times more furious, and more puissant°,   *mighty*
Unmindful of his wound of his fate ignorant.[47]

35

So both at once him charge on either side,
With hideous strokes, and importable power,
That forced him his ground to traverse wide,
And wisely watch to ward that deadly stower°:   *attack*
For in his shield, as thick as stormy shower,
Their strokes did rain, yet did he never quail,
Nor backward shrink, but as a steadfast tower,

42. Arthur's spear pierces Pyrochle's (Guyon's) shield and gores his shoulder.

43. This oath is either on an ancient city in Spain, Mahon, the false prophet Moham-
med, or a new brand of toothpaste.

44. I.e., "You'll pay for that."

45. Arthur nearly missed having his head chopped in two. He knows when to roll,
and he dives from his horse to avoid being mincemeat.

46. Prince Arthur is in a tight spot having only a spear against two large and angry
knights. Even one of them would have been a match for any knight.

47. Pyrochles, wounded in the shoulder, is madder than ever and goes after Arthur.

Whom foe with double battery doth assail,
Them on her bulwark bears, and bids them naught avail.

36

So stoutly he withstood their strong assay,
Till that at last, when he advantage spied,
His poignant° spear he thrust with puissant° sway   *affective / mighty*
At proud Cymochles, whiles his shield was wide,
That through his thigh the mortal steel did gryde°:   *pierce*
He swerving with the force, within his flesh
Did break the lance, and let the head abide:
Out of the wound the red blood flowed fresh,
That underneath his feet soon made a purple plesh°.[48]   *pool*

37

Horribly then he 'gan to rage, and rail,
Cursing his gods and himself damning deep:
Als° when his brother saw the red blood rail   *also*
Down so fast, and all his armor steep,
For very fellness loud he 'gan to weep,
And said, "Caitiff°, curse on thy cruel hand,   *cowardly fool*
That twice hath sped; yet shall it not thee keep
From the third brunt of this my fatal brand:
Lo where the dreadful death behind thy back doth stand."

38

With that he stroke, and the other stroke withal,
That nothing seemed mote° bear so monstrous might: *might*
The one upon his covered shield did fall,
And glancing down would not his owner bite:
But the other did upon his truncheon° smite,   *spear shaft*
Which hewing quite asunder, further way
It made, and on his haqueton° did light°,   *mail coat / land*
The which dividing with importune sway,
It seized in his right side, and there the dint did stay.[49]

48. Arthur withstands the onslaught of both knights for a time, and when an opening appears he lands his spear in the thigh of Cymocles and breaks the head of the spear, leaving it in his leg.

49. The sword still refuses to give any mortal blow to Arthur, but Arthur, only having the shaft of his spear, finally receives a stroke from Pyrochles. It's no accident that he receives a wound to the side: he represents Christ fighting for His people.

39

Wide was the wound and a large lukewarm flood,
Red as the rose, thence gushed grievously;
That when the paynim° spied the streaming blood,   *pagan*
Gave him great heart and hope of victory.
On the other side, in huge perplexity,
The Prince now stood, having his weapon broke;
Naught could he hurt, but still at ward° did lie: *guard*
Yet with his truncheon° he so rudely stroke   *spear shaft*
Cymochles twice, that twice him forced his foot revoke.⁵⁰

40

Whom when the Palmer saw in such distress,
Sir Guyon's sword he lightly to him wrought,
And said, "Fair son, great God thy right hand bless,
To use that sword so wisely as it ought.
Glad was the knight and with fresh courage fraught,
When as again he arméd felt his hand;
Then like a lion which hath long time sought
His robbed whelps° and at the last them found   *young*
Amongst the shepherd swains°, then waxeth   *boys*
   wood° and yond°.⁵¹   *mad / fierce*

41

So fierce he laid about him, and dealt blows
On either side, that neither mail could hold,
Nor shield defend the thunder of his throws:
Now to Pyrochles many strokes he told;
Eft° to Cymochles twice so many fold: *then*
Then back again turning his busy hand,
Them both at once compelled with courage bold,
To yield wide way to his heart-thrilling brand;
And though they both stood stiff, yet could not both withstand.

42

As savage bull, whom two fierce mastiffs⁵² bait,
When rancor° doth with rage him once engore,   *fury*

50. Swinging what is left of his spear, he makes Cymochles back up twice.
51. The Palmer, better late than never, gives Arthur Guyon's sword. He immediately resumes his prowess and begins tearing through like an angry lion that finds shepherd boys have taken its cubs.
52. To put it simply, a mastiff is a big dog. One word: Magnus.

Forgets with wary ward them to await,
But with his dreadful horns them drives afore,
Or flings aloft, or treads down in the floor,
Breathing out wrath, and bellowing disdain,
That all the forest quakes to hear him roar:
So raged Prince Arthur twixt° his foemen twain,   *between*
That neither could his mighty puissance° sustain.   *strength*

43

But ever at Pyrochles when he smit°,   *dealt blows*
Who Guyon's shield cast ever him before,
Whereon the Faerie Queene's portrait was writ,
His hand relented, and the stroke forbore,
And his dear heart the picture 'gan adore,
Which oft the paynim° saved from deadly stower°.⁵³   *pagan / blow*
But him henceforth the same can save no more;
For now arrivéd is his fatal hour,
That no'te° avoided be by earthly skill or power.   *could not*

44

For when Cymochles saw the foul reproach,
Which them appeached°, pricked with guilty shame,   *attacked*
And inward grief, he fiercely 'gan approach,
Resolved to put away that loathely blame,
Or die with honor and desert of fame;
And on the hauberk° stroke the Prince so sore,   *armor*
That quite disparted all the linked frame,
And pierced to the skin, but bit no more,
Yet made him twice to reel, that never moved afore.⁵⁴

45

Whereat reinfierced with wrath and sharp regret,
He stroke so hugely with his borrowed blade,
That it empierced the pagan's burganet°,   *helmet*
And cleaving the hard steel did deep invade
Into his head, and cruel passage made
Quite through his brain.⁵⁵ He tumbling down on ground,

53. Arthur takes it easy when dealing blows to Guyon's shield (Pyrochles was holding it) because it has the Faerie Queene's image on it.

54. After Arthur has dealt blow after blow sending the brothers backwards, Cymochles finally decides to give Athur his best shot or die trying. His stroke pierces Arthur's armor, but it doesn't break the skin.

55. Bye-bye, Cymochles.

Breathéd out his ghost, which to the infernal shade
Fast flying, there eternal torment found,
For all the sins wherewith his lewd° life did abound.   *immoral*

46

Which when his german° saw, the stony fear   *brother*
Ran to his heart and all his sense dismayed,
Nor thenceforth life nor courage did appear,
But as a man, whom hellish fiends have frayed°,   *frightened*
Long trembling still he stood: at last thus said,
"Traitor what hast thou done? How ever may
Thy curséd hand so cruelly have swayed
Against that knight: harrow and well away,
After so wicked deed why livest thou longer day?"

47

With that all desperate as loathing light,
And with revenge desiring soon to die,
Assembling all his force and utmost might,
With his own sword he fierce at him did fly,
And struck and foined° and lashed outrageously,   *thrust*
Withouten reason or regard. Well knew
The Prince, with patience and sufferance sly
So hasty heat soon cooled to subdue:
Though when this breathless wax[56] that battle 'gan renew.

48

As when a windy tempest bloweth high,
That nothing may withstand his stormy stower°,   *blast*
The clouds, as things afraid, before him fly;
But all so soon as his outrageous power
Is laid, they fiercely then begin to shower,
And as in scorn of his spent stormy spite,
Now all at once their malice forth do pour;
So did Prince Arthur bear himself in fight,
And suffered rash Pyrochles waste his idle might.[57]

56. I.e., when he caught his breath.
57. Prince Arthur just hangs out. He's letting Pyrochles waste his energy.

49

At last when as the Saracen° perceived,   *Muslim*
How that strange sword refused to serve his need,
But when he stroke most strong, the dint deceived,
He flung it from him, and devoid of dread,
Upon him lightly leaping without heed,
Twixt his two mighty arms engraspéd fast°,   *tight*
Thinking to overthrow and down him tread:
But him in strength and skill the Prince surpassed,
And through his nimble sleight° did under him down cast.[58] *movement*

50

Naught booted° it the paynim° then to strive;[59] *helped / pagan*
For as a bittern[60] in the eagle's claw,
That may not hope by flight to scape° alive,   *escape*
Still waits for death with dread and trembling awe;
So he now subject to the victor's law,
Did not once move nor upward cast his eye,
For vile disdain and rancor which did gnaw
His heart in twain with sad melancholy,
As one that loathéd life and yet despised to die.

51

But full of princely bounty and great mind,
The conqueror naught cared him to slay,
But casting wrongs and all revenge behind,
More glory thought to give life than decay,
And said, "Paynim°, this is thy dismal day;   *Pagan*
Yet if thou wilt renounce thy miscreance°, *evil way of life*
And my true liegeman yield thyself for aye°,   *forever*
Life will I grant thee for thy valiance°,   *chivalry*
And all thy wrongs will wipe out of my sovenance°."[61] *remembrance*

58. Pyrochles finally realizes that the sword is under a spell. Every stroke resists his might and refuses to strike its master. So Pyrochles flings the sword away from him and dives at Arthur, hoping to catch him in his arms and give him the oh-so-deadly "bear hug of death." But Arthur simply sidesteps the madman, and Pyrochles gets arms full of air.

59. I.e., it was no use for the heathen to keep fighting.

60. A bittern is a wading bird with brown plumage and a deep cry.

61. I.e., "If you give up your evil deeds and swear allegiance to me, then I'll wipe your slate clean."

52

"Fool," said the pagan, "I thy gift defy,
But use thy fortune as it doth befall,
And say, that I not overcome do die,
But in despite of life for death do call."
Wroth was the Prince, and sorry yet with all,
That he so willfully refuséd grace;
Yet since his fate so cruélly did fall,   *since*
His shining helmet he 'gan soon unlace,
And left his headless body bleeding all the place.[62]

53

By this Sir Guyon from his trance awaked,
Life having mastered her senseless foe;
And looking up, when as his shield he lacked,
And sword saw not, he waxéd wondrous woe:[63]
But when the Palmer, whom he long ago
Had lost, he by him spied, right glad he grew,
And said, "Dear sir, whom wandering to and fro
I long have lacked, I joy thy face to view;
Firm is thy faith whom danger never fro° me drew.   *from*

54

"But read° what wicked hand hath robbéd me   *tell*
Of my good sword and shield?" The Palmer glad,
With so fresh hue uprising him to see,
Him answered; "Fair son, be no wit sad
For want° of weapons, they shall soon be had."   *lack*
So 'gan he to discourse the whole debate,
Which that strange knight for him sustainéd had,
And those two Saracens° confounded late,   *Muslims*
Whose carcasses on ground were horribly prostrate.[64]

62. Pyrochles calls Arthur a fool and says he'd rather die. And Arthur gives him his wish. Bye-bye, Pyrochles.

63. That is to say, he grew a bit worried when he realized he was missing both his sword and shield.

64. Guyon is glad to see the Palmer again, having been without him for some time. Guyon asks him what happened and where his sword and shield are. And the Palmer reviews the whole story, pointing to the dead bodies of Pyrochles and Cymochles.

55

Which when he heard and saw the tokens true,
His heart with great affection was imbued°,   *filled*
And to the Prince bowing with reverence due,
As to the patron of his life, thus said;
"My Lord, my liege, by whose most gracious aid
I live this day, and see my foes subdued,
What may suffice° to be for meed° repaid   *be enough / reward*
Of so great graces, as ye have me showed,
But to be ever bound."

56

To whom the Infant thus, "Fair sir, what need
Good turns be counted as a servile° bond,   *slave*
To bind their doers, to receive their meed°?   *reward*
Are not all knights by oath bound to withstand
Oppressors power by arms and puissant° hand?   *mighty*
Suffice° that I have done my due in place."[65]   *it's enough*
So goodly purpose they together found,
Of kindness and of courteous grace;
The whiles false Archimage and Atin fled apace.[66]

65. The "Infant" is Prince Arthur. This does not mean that he was a baby and sucked his thumb. This term is an old word and could refer to anyone of noble birth. When Guyon asks how he may repay him, Arthur says he was just doing his duty.

66. Run away! Run away! Archimago and Atin take this opportunity to do some distance running.

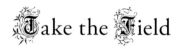ake the ield

Directions: Identify where in the story the following quotes came from. Explain what they mean and their significance to the story.

1. "Yet gold all is not, that doth golden seem,
   Nor all good knights, that shake well spear and shield:
   The worth of all men by their end esteem,
   And then due praise, or due reproach them yield."

2. "Honor is least where odds appeareth most."

3. "Traitor what hast thou done? How ever may
   Thy curséd hand so cruelly have swayed
   Against that knight: harrow and well away,
   After so wicked deed why livest thou longer day?"

Canto IX.

The house of Temperance, in which
doth sober Alma dwell,
Besieged of many foes, whom stranger
knights to flight compel.

1

Of all God's works which do this world adorn,
There is no one more fair and excellent,
Than is man's body both for power and form,
Whiles it is kept in sober government;
But none than it, more foul and indecent,
Distempered through misrule and passions base:
It grows a monster, and incontinent
Doth loose his dignity and native grace.
Behold, who list°, both one and other in this place.[1]   *desire*

2

After the paynim° brethren conquered were,   *pagan*
The Briton Prince recovering his stolen sword,
And Guyon his lost shield, they both affair
Forth passed on their way in fair accord,
Till him the Prince with gentle court did board°;   *inquire*

1. Spenser introduces this canto describing how amazing the human body is as long as it is ruled with temperance. Intemperance makes the body monstrous. Spenser says we'll get a chance to observe both of these in this canto.

"Sir knight, mote° I of you this courtesy read°,   *might / receive*
To weet° why on your shield so goodly scored   *know*
 Bear ye the picture of that lady's head?

3

"Full lively is the semblant°, though the substance dead."[2]   *likeness*
"Fair sir," said he, "if in that picture dead
 Such life ye read, and virtue in vain show,
What might ye ween°, if the true lively-head   *think*
 Of that most glorious visage ye did view?
 But if the beauty of her mind ye knew,
That is her bounty, and imperial power,
 Thousand times fairer than her mortal hue,
 O how great wonder would your thoughts devour,
And infinite desire into your spirit pour!

4

"She is the mighty Queene of Faerie,
 Whose fair retrait° I in my shield do bear;   *portrait*
 She is the flower of grace and chastity,
Throughout the world renowned far and near,
 My lief°, my liege, my sovereign, my dear,   *beloved*
 Whose glory shineth as the morning star,
And with her light the earth illumines clear;
 Far reach her mercies and her praises far,
As well in state of peace, as puissance° in war."[3]   *fierceness*

5

"Thrice happy man," said then the Briton knight
"Whom gracious lot, and thy great valiance
 Have made thee soldier of that princess bright,
Which with her bounty and glad countenance
 Doth bless her servants, and them high advance.
 How may strange knight hope ever to aspire,
By faithful service, and meet eminence,
 Unto such bliss? Sufficient were that hire
For loss of thousand lives, to die at her desire."[4]

  2. The Prince and Guyon travel for a while, and the Prince asks Guyon about the image of the woman on Guyon's shield and notes how real the picture looks.
  3. The woman on Guyon's shield is the Faerie Queene, renowned far and wide.
  4. Arthur believes Guyon to be very blessed to be in the service of the Faerie Queene.

6

Said Guyon, "Noble lord, what meed° so great,   *reward*
Or grace of earthly prince so sovereign,
But by your wondrous worth and warlike feat
Ye well may hope, and easily attain?
But were your will, her sold to entertain,
And numbered be 'mongst knights of Maidenhead,
Great guerdon°, well I wote°, should you remain,   *reward / know*
And in her favor high be reckoned,
As Arthegall, and Sophy now been honoréd."[5]

7

"Certes°," then said the Prince, "I God avow,   *certainly*
That since I arms and knighthood first did plight°,   *join*
My whole desire hath been, and yet is now,
To serve that Queene with all my power and might.
Now hath the sun with his lamp-burning light,
Walked round about the world, and I no less,
Since of that Goddess I have sought the sight,
Yet no where can her find: such happiness
Heaven doth to me envy, and fortune favorless."[6]

8

"Fortune, the foe of famous chevisance°   *chivalry*
Seldom" said Guyon "yields to virtue aid,
But in her way throws mischief and mischance,
Whereby her course is stopped, and passage stayed.
But you, fair sir, be not herewith dismayed,
But constant keep the way, in which ye stand;
Which were it not, that I am else delayed
With hard adventure, which I have in hand,
I labor would to guide you through all Faerie Land."[7]

5. Guyon assures Arthur that he would be well received in the service of the Faerie
Queene. Arthegall is hero of Book V of *The Faerie Queene,* and we suspect that Sophy
was another who was to be written into a future book.
6. This has been Arthur's quest for the last year: to find the Faerie Queene and pledge
himself to her service. But so far he's not been successful.
7. Guyon says that if he was not already preoccupied with his current mission, he
would be happy to show Arthur around Faerie Land and (presumably) take him to the
Queene.

9

"Gramercy° sir," said he, "but mote° I wote°,   *thank you / might / know*
What strange adventure do ye now pursue?
Perhaps my succor° or advisement meet°   *help / fitting advice*
Mote stead you much your purpose to subdue."[8]
Then 'gan Sir Guyon all the story show
Of false Acrasia, and her wicked wiles,
Which to avenge, the Palmer him forth drew
From Faerie court. So talked they, the whiles
They wasted had much way, and measured many miles.

10

And now fair Phoebus 'gan decline in haste
His weary wagon to the western vale,[9]
When as they spied a goodly castle, placed
Foreby a river in a pleasant dale°,   *valley*
Which choosing for that evening's hospital°,   *hotel*
They thither marched: but when they came in sight,
And from their sweaty coursers° did avail°,   *horses / dismount*
They found the gates fast barred long ere° night,   *before*
And every loop fast locked, as fearing foes despite.

11

Which when they saw, they weened° foul reproach   *thought*
Was to them done, their entrance to forestall,
Till that the Squire 'gan nigher° to approach;   *nearer*
And wind° his horn under the castle wall,   *blow*
That with the noise it shook, as it would fall:
Eftsoones° forth looked from the highest spire   *presently*
The watch, and loud unto the knights did call,
To weet°, what they so rudely did require.   *know*
Who gently answered, They entrance did desire.[10]

12

"Fly, fly, good knights," said he "fly fast away
If that your lives ye love, as meet° ye should;   *fitting*

---

8. I.e., "Maybe I can steady your purpose."
9. The sun is going down.
10. So after many miles, they reach a castle that seems like a nice place to stay. But the castle is all locked and shut up. Arthur's squire is finally able to get the inhabitants' attention by blowing his horn.

Fly fast, and save yourselves from near decay,
Here may ye not have entrance, though we would:
We would and would again, if that we could;
But thousand enemies about us rave,
And with long siege us in this castle hold:
Seven years this wise they us besiegéd have,
And many good knights slain, that have us sought to save."[11]

13

Thus as he spoke, lo with outrageous cry
A thousand villains round about them swarmed
Out of the rocks and caves adjoining nigh,
Vile caitiff° wretches, ragged, rude, deformed,   *cowardly*
All threatening death, all in strange manner armed,
Some with unwieldy clubs, some with long spears,
Some rusty knives, some staves in fire warmed.
Stern was their look, like wild amazéd stares,
Staring with hollow eyes, and stiff upstanding hairs.[12]

14

Fiercely at first those knights they did assail,
And drove them to recoil: but when again
They gave fresh charge, their forces 'gan to fail,
Unable their encounter to sustain;
For with such puissance° and impetuous main°   *strength / attack*
Those champions broke on them, that forced them fly,
Like scattered sheep, whenas the shepherd's swain°   *servant*
A lion and a tiger doth espy°,   *see*
With greedy pace forth rushing from the forest nigh.[13]

15

A while they fled, but soon returned again
With greater fury, than before was found;

11. "Run! Run!" The watchman calls. He says they would happily entertain them any other time, but they are surrounded by enemies that have done great evils to them and other visitors.

12. Spiked hair and hollow eyes . . . they probably appeared on MTV in their spare time.

13. These man-beasts swarm around Guyon, the Palmer, Arthur, and his squire and for a moment drive them back. But the four quickly regain their footing and break through the creatures' lines, sending them back running.

And evermore their cruel captain
Sought with his rascal routs to enclose them round,
And overrun to tread them to the ground.
But soon the knights with their bright-burning blades
Broke their rude troops, and orders did confound,
Hewing and slashing at their idle shades;
For though they bodies seem, yet substance from them fades.

16

As when a swarm of gnats at eventide
Out of the fens° of Allan do arise,   *bogs*
Their murmuring small trumpets sounding wide,
Whiles in the air their clustering army flies,
That as a cloud doth seem to dim the skies;
Nor man nor beast may rest, or take repast°,   *a meal*
For their sharp wounds, and noyous° injuries,   *annoying*
Till the fierce northern wind with blustering blast
Doth blow them quite away, and in the ocean cast.[14]

17

Thus when they had that troublous rout dispersed,
Unto the castle gate they come again,
And entrance craved°, which was denied erst°.   *requested / before*
Now when report of that their perilous pain,
And cumbrous° conflict, which they did sustain,   *cumbersome*
Came to the lady's ear, which there did dwell,
She forth issued with a goodly train
Of squires and ladies equipaged[15] well,
And entertained them right fairly, as befell.[16]

18

Alma[17] she called was, a virgin bright;
That had not yet felt Cupid's wanton rage,
Yet was she wooed of many a gentle knight,

14. The armies are finally scattered like obnoxious insects.
15. They're loaded with tea and other entertaining necessities like baseball cards and root beer.
16. I.e., They said, "Hey, you know those armies? Yeah, well . . . they're gone." She said, "Won't you please come in?"
17. Alma, for reasons that will become obvious in the following pages, represents the "pure soul." Her name means "soul" in Italian and "virgin" in Hebrew.

And many a lord of noble parentage,
That sought with her to link in marriage:
For she was fair, as fair might ever be,
And in the flower now of her freshest age;
Yet full of grace and goodly modesty,
That even heaven rejoicéd her sweet face to see.

19

In robe of lily white she was arrayed,
That from her shoulder to her heel down raught°,   *reached*
The train whereof loose far behind her strayed,
Branched with gold and pearl, most richly wrought,
And born of two fair damsels, which were taught,
That service well. Her yellow golden hair
Was trimly woven, and in tresses wrought,
Nor other tire° she on her head did wear,   *attire*
But crowned with a garland of sweet rosier.[18]

20

Goodly she entertained those noble knights,
And brought them up into her castle hall;
Where gentle court and gracious delight
She to them made, with mildness virginal,[19]
Showing herself both wise and liberal:[20]
There when they rested had a season due,
They her besought of favor special,
Of that fair castle to afford them view;
She granted, and them leading forth, the same did show.[21]

21

First she them led up to the castle wall,
That was so high, as foe might not it climb,
And all so fair, and fencable withal°,   *altogether fortified*
Not built of brick, nor yet of stone and lime,
But of thing like to that Egyptian slime,

---

18. That's a sweet briar of sorts.

19. I.e., she was courteous and modest.

20. Liberal means "free," even though many moderns use the term to describe a kind of militant immorality.

21. She gives them some snacks and lets them rest, but very soon they ask her to show them around the castle.

Whereof king Nine[22] whilome° built Babel tower;   *formerly*
But O great pity, that no longer time
So goodly workmanship should not endure:
Soon it must turn to earth; no earthly thing is sure.[23]

                              22
The frame thereof seemed partly circular,
And part triangular, O work divine;
Those two the first and last proportions are,
The one imperfect, mortal, feminine;
The other immortal, perfect, masculine,
And twixt them both a quadrate was the base,
Proportioned equally by seven and nine;
Nine was the circle set in heaven's place,
All which compacted made a goodly diapase.[24]

                              23
Therein two gates were placéd seemly well:
The one before, by which all in did pass,
Did the other far in workmanship excel;
For not of wood, nor of enduring brass,
But of more worthy substance framed it was;
Doubly disported°, it did lock and close,   *supported*
That when it locked, none might thorough° pass,   *through*
And when it opened, no man might it close,
Still open to their friends, and closed to their foes.[25]

                              24
Of hewn stone the porch was fairly wrought,
Stone more of value, and more smooth and fine,

   22. King Nine, or Ninus, was the legendary founder of Babylon. The Bible gives the man's name as Nimrod (Gen. 10:8–10). Perhaps they're the same guy.
   23. Now here's where you've got to start paying attention. This "castle" that Alma inhabits is Spenser's commentary on the human body. Notice the details of shape, disposition, the servants (and their jobs), and the rest. There are also bits that won't make much sense, as the descriptions are allusions to medieval conceptions of physiology and psychology, which for the most part, are odd mixtures of Plato, Aristotle, and Christianity.
   24. That means rich harmony. All those bits about geometry and numbers describe the classical and medieval conception of a well-balanced/proportioned man. Seven was the perfect number of the earth, and nine was supposed to be the number of levels in heaven (See Dante's *Paradiso* in *The Divine Comedy*). Thus "diapase" or rich harmony.
   25. What part of the body is that? The mouth.

Than jet or marble far from Ireland brought;
Over the which was cast a wandering vine,
Enchaced° with a wanton ivy twine.   *interwoven*
And over it a fair portcullis²⁶ hung,
Which to the gate directly did incline,
With comely compass, and compacture strong,²⁷
Neither unseemly short, nor yet exceeding long.

25

Within the barbican° a Porter sat,   *drawbridge tower*
Day and night duly keeping watch and ward,
Nor wight°, nor word mote° pass out of the gate,   *creature / might*
But in good order, and with due regard;
Utterers of secrets he from thence debarred,
Babblers of folly, and blazers of crime.²⁸
His larumbell° might loud and wide be heard,   *alarm bell*
When cause required, but never out of time;
Early and late it rung, at evening and at prime°.   *dawn*

26

And round about the porch on every side
Twice sixteen warders sat, all armed bright
In glistering steel, and strongly fortified:
Tall yeomen seemed they, and of great might,
And were enranged° ready, still for fight.²⁹   *arranged*
By them as Alma passed with her guests,
They did obeisance, as beseemed right,³⁰
And then again returned to their rests:
The Porter eke° to her did lout° with humble jests.   *also / bow*

26. This is the set of wooden or iron bars that hang down in a gateway for fortification. It can be lowered to block entrance. Here the portcullis represents the lips. You know, the better to kiss you with.

27. They are strongly knit together.

28. Notice how the Porter guards against idle babble, gossip, and other intemperate speech.

29. This is the oral cavity, or as they call in it in the old country: the mouth. And those "twice sixteen warders" are the teeth.

30. I.e., they showed her due honor as she passed.

27

Thence she them brought into a stately hall,
Wherein were many tables fair dispread,
And ready dight° with drapets° festival,   *covered / linens*
Against the viands° should be ministered.   *dishes of food*
At the upper end there sat, yclad° in red   *clad*
Down to the ground, a comely personage,
That in his hand a white rod managed,
He steward was hight° Diet; ripe of age,   *called*
And in demeanor sober, and in counsel sage.[31]

28

And through the hall there walked to and fro[32]
A jolly yeoman, marshall of the same,
Whose name was Appetite; he did bestow
Both guests and meat, whenever in they came,
And knew them how to order without blame,
As him the steward bade. They both at one
Did duty to their lady, as became;
Who passing by, forth led her guests anon°   *at once*
Into the kitchen room, nor spared for niceness none.

29

It was a vat ybuilt° for great dispence,[33]   *built*
With many ranges reared along the wall;
And one great chimney, whose long tunnel thence,
The smoke forth threw. And in the midst of all
There placed was a cauldron wide and tall,
Upon a mighty furnace, burning hot,
More hot, than Aetn', or flaming Mongiball:[34]
For day and night it burned, nor ceased not,
So long as any thing it in the cauldron got.

30

But to delay the heat, least by mischance
It might break out, and set the whole on fire,

31. Hmmm. Let's see. It's red, likes food . . . what do you figure that represents?
32. The hall is the throat. Eh?
33. You could put lots of stuff in it. Hello, Mr. Stomach.
34. Mount Aetna was a volcano. Mongiball was a prototype of baseball. Bases were called "mongis" because they were small rodents from Mongolia. This made the game a bit more exciting but certainly less organized. The genius of stationary "bases" was discovered when mongis began dying in a sudden mongi-itis outbreak in 1714. Or maybe not.

There added was by goodly ordinance,
An huge great pair of bellows, which did stire[35]
Continually, and cooling breath inspire.
About the cauldron many cooks coiled,[36]
With hooks and ladles, as need did require;
The whiles the viands° in the vessel boiled   *dishes of food*
They did about their business sweat, and sorely toiled.

31

The master cook was called Concoction,
A careful man, and full of comely guise:
The kitchen clerk, that hight° Digestion,   *named*
Did order all the achates[37] in seemly wise,
And set them forth, as well he could devise.
The rest had several offices° assigned,   *jobs*
Some to remove the scum, as it did rise;
Others to bear the same away did mind;
And others it to use according to his kind.

32

But all the liquor, which was foul and waste,
Not good nor serviceable else for ought,
They in another great round vessel placed,
Till by a conduit pipe it thence were brought:
And all the rest, that noyous° was, and naught°,   *nuisance / nothing*
By secret ways, that none might it espy°,   *see*
Was close conveyed, and to the back-gate brought,
That clepped° was Port Esquiline,[38] whereby   *called*
It was avoided quite, and thrown out privily°.[39]   *privately*

33

Which goodly order, and great workman's skill
When as those knights beheld, with rare delight,
And gazing wonder they their minds did fill;

---

35. That's stir, meaning "pump."

36. Those are supposed to be the intestines.

37. Achates was the faithful companion of Aeneas in the *Aeneid* of Virgil. Here it means just "loyal friends."

38. Esquiline was one of the seven hills of ancient Rome. It was there that Nero had his Golden House and Trajan had his warm baths.

39. That's Spenser's description how the body eliminates waste.

For never had they seen so strange a sight.[40]
Thence back again fair Alma led them right,
And soon into a goodly parlor brought,
That was with royal arrays richly dight°,   *decorated*
In which was nothing portrayed, nor wrought,
Not wrought, nor portrayed, but easy to be thought.[41]

34

 And in the midst thereof upon the floor,
A lovely bevy° of fair ladies sat,   *group*
Courted of many a jolly paramour°,   *lover*
The which them did in modest wise° amate°,   *manner / pair off*
And each one sought his lady to aggrate°:   *please*
And eke° amongst them little Cupid played   *also*
His wanton sports, being returned late
From his fierce wars, and having from him laid
His cruél bow, wherewith he thousands hath dismayed.

35

Diverse delights they found themselves to please;
Some sung in sweet consort, some laughed for joy,
Some played with straws, some idly sat at ease;
But other some could not abide to toy,
All pleasance was to them grief and annoy:
This frowned, that fawned, the third for shame did blush,
Another seemed envious, or coy,
Another in her teeth did gnaw a rush:
But at these strangers presence everyone did hush.[42]

36

Soon as the gracious Alma came in place,
They all at once out of their seats arose,
And to her homage made, with humble grace:
Whom when the knights beheld, they 'gan dispose
Themselves to court, and each a damsel chose:
The Prince by chance did on a lady light,

40. Yup. Pretty strange castle, wouldn't you say?
41. And what might that mean? Not sure. But the parlor represents the heart. It has been suggested that those lines refer to the imagination.
42. All these ladies represent the different tendencies of the heart or emotions, both for good and evil. But they all grow quiet when Guyon, Arthur, and company arrive.

That was right fair and fresh as morning rose,
But somewhat sad, and solemn eke° in sight,   *also*
As if some pensive thought constrained her gentle spright°.[43]   *spirit*

37

In a long purple pall°, whose skirt with gold,   *dark covering*
Was fretted all about, she was arrayed;
And in her hand a Poplar branch did hold:
To whom the Prince in courteous manner said;
"Gentle madam, why been ye thus dismayed,
And your fair beauty do with sadness spill?
Lives any, that you hath thus ill paid?
Or do you love, or do you lack your will?
Whatever be the cause, it sure beseems you ill."

38

"Fair sir," said she half in disdainful wise,
"How is it, that this mood in me ye blame,
And in yourself do not the same advise?
Him ill beseems, another's fault to name,
That may unawares be blotted with the same:
Pensive I yield I am, and sad in mind,
Through great desire of glory and of fame:
Nor ought I ween° are ye therein behind,   *think*
That have twelve months sought one, yet no where can her find."

39

The Prince was inly° moved at her speech,   *inwardly*
Well weeting° true, what she had rashly told;   *thinking*
Yet with fair semblant° sought to hide the breach,   *appearance*
Which change of color did perforce unfold,
Now seeming flaming hot, now stony cold.
Though turning soft aside, he did inquire,
What wight° she was, that Poplar branch did hold: *person*
It answered was, her name was Praise-Desire,
That by well doing sought to honor to aspire.[44]

43. The two gentlemen, being polite, take up conversations with two ladies. The Prince begins talking to a woman who seems very serious, maybe even a bit upset.

44. Her name is Praise-Desire. She tells Arthur that she is a bit pensive, but no more than he because he has been searching for the Faerie Queene for the last year. She's a bit rude. But Arthur takes it all in stride.

40

The whiles, the Faerie knight[45] did entertain
Another damsel of that gentle crew,
That was right fair, and modest of demean°,   *conduct*
But that too oft she changed her native hue:
Strange was her tire°, and all her garment blue,   *attire*
Close round about her tucked with many a plight°:   *fold*
Upon her fist the bird, which shunneth view,
And keeps in coverts close from living wight°,   *creature*
Did sit, as yet ashamed, how rude Pan did her dight.[46]

41

So long as Guyon with her commoned°,   *accompanied*
Unto the ground she cast her modest eye,
And ever and anon with rosy red
The bashful blood her snowy cheeks did dye,
That her became, as polished ivory,
Which cunning craftsman hand hath overlaid
With fair vermilion° or pure castory°.   *red / brown oil*
Great wonder had the knight, to see the maid[47]
So strangely passioned, and to her gently said,

42

"Fair Damsel, seemeth, by your troubled cheer,
That either me too bold ye ween°, this wise   *think*
You to molest°, or other ill to fear   *bother*
That in the secret of your heart close lies,
From whence it doth, as cloud from sea arise.
If it be I, of pardon I you pray;
But if ought else that I mote° not devise,   *might*
I will, if please you it discure°, assay°,   *describe / tell me*
To ease you of that ill, so wisely as I may."

43

She answered naught, but more abashed for shame,
Held down her head, the whiles her lovely face

---

45. The Faerie knight is of course Guyon.

46. Pan, the Roman god of woods, fields and flocks, clothed her. He had a man's torso and head, but he had a goat's legs, horns and ears. She's dressed rude, meaning "wildly" and "unattractively." There's a bird sitting on her hand.

47. This lady keeps blushing and looking down and away. She isn't a very good conversationalist.

The flashing blood with blushing did inflame,
And the strong passion marred her modest grace,
That Guyon marveled at her uncouth° case: *improper*
Till Alma him bespake, "Why wonder ye
Fair sir at that, which ye so much embrace?
She is the fountain of your modesty;
You shamefacéd are, but Shamefacedness itself is she."

44

Thereat the elf° did blush in privity,   *Guyon*
And turned his face away; but she the same
Dissembled fair, and feigned to oversee.[48]
Thus they awhile with court and goodly game,
Themselves did solace each one with his dame,
Till that great lady thence away them sought,
To view her castle's other wondrous frame.
Up to a stately turret she them brought,
Ascending by ten steps of alabaster wrought.

45

That turret's frame most admirable was,
Like highest heaven compassed around,
And lifted high above this earthly mass,
Which it surveyed, as hills do lower ground;
But not on ground mote° like to this be found,   *might*
Not that, which antique Cadmus[49] whilome° built   *formerly*
In Thebes, which Alexander did confound;
Nor that proud tower of Troy, though richly gilt°,   *adorned*
From which young Hector's blood by cruél Greeks was spilt.[50]

46

The roof hereof was arched overhead,
And decked with flowers and herbars[51] daintily;
Two goodly beacons, set in watches stead,
Therein gave light, and flamed continually:
For they of living fire most subtly

48. Guyon, like Arthur, has met his own "passion" or "emotion," Shamefacedness.
49. He was a Phoenician prince who founded Thebes, a city in Greece.
50. They're ascending up the neck. Careful, don't gurgle.
51. That refers generally to a number of different kinds of plants. This seems to be Spenser's reference to hair.

Were made, and set in silver sockets bright,
Covered with lids devised of substance sly,
That readily they shut and open might.
O who can tell the praises of that Maker's might!⁵²

47

Nor can I tell, nor can I stay to tell
This parts great workmanship, and wondrous power,
That all this other worlds work doth excel,
And likest is unto that heavenly tower,
That God hath built for his own blessed bower.
Therein were diverse rooms, and diverse stages,
But three the chiefest, and of greatest power,
In which there dwelt three honorable sages,
The wisest men, I ween°, that lived in their ages.   *know*

48

Not he, whom Greece, the nurse of all good arts,
By Phoebus' doom, the wisest thought alive,
Might be compared to these by many parts:
Nor that sage Pylian sire, which did survive
Three ages, such as mortal men contrive,
By whose advice old Priam's city fell,
With these in praise of policies mote° strive.   *might*
These three in these three rooms did sundry° dwell,   *apart*
And counseled fair Alma, how to govern well.⁵³

49

The first of them could things to come foresee:
The next could of things present best advise;
The third things past could keep in memory,
So that no time, nor reason could arise,
But that the same could one of these comprise.
Forthy° the first did in the forepart sit,⁵⁴   *therefore*
That naught mote° hinder his quick prejudice: *might*

52. Spenser exclaims with joy at the wonder of the eye and He who made it.
53. These three wise men who live in the "head" counsel Alma and represent different parts of the brain.
54. The first wise man's name is Phantastes (his name will be given in a couple of stanzas). He is the part of the brain that we call the imagination or creativity where all sorts of wonderful and awful things can exist, depending on our care.

Angels

What are angels? The Bible describes for us several kinds of angels or angelic beings. It is commonly understood that angels are messengers, guardians, and servants of God. They bring judgments and greetings, declarations and disasters. Angels are described in the Bible as beings who rule over the world as the ambassadors of God. Of particular interest is what these angels look like. Unfortunately, the Renaissance (among other things) has supplied us with an endless supply of Hallmark images of angels as fat babies with wings and bow and arrows. But this is simply not the case. The seraphim are angelic beings that probably look a lot like what we would call a dragon. These are described as having six wings and being serpent-like (Is. 6:2; cf. Num. 21:6). Other angelic beings are the cherubim. Cherubim are creatures described as having four faces and four wings. Their faces are of a man, lion, ox, and eagle (Ezek. 10:14–21). They are the guardians of the Garden of Eden when Adam and Eve are sent into exile, and they continue to guard the Most Holy Place in the Tabernacle and the Temple. Angels sometimes also appear in the form of a man (e.g., Dan. 9:21), and often these appearances are theophanies of the pre-incarnate Son of God (e.g., Gen. 32:24–30). However, in every instance we have of such an appearance, the person to whom they appear is never tempted to say, "Aw, how cute!" The reaction throughout Scripture is uniformly one of awe and reverence and usually terror. Angels and angelic beings are noble and monstrous creatures. They inspire fear and trepidation and are completely awe inspiring. Of course, the faithful of God have nothing to truly fear from these, His servants, but it is always good to be reminded that we serve a wonderful and terrible God. And His messenger-guardians are no less so.

He had a sharp foresight, and working wit,
That never idle was, nor once could rest a wit.

50

His chamber was dispainted° all within,   *painted*
With sundry colors, in the which were writ°   *written*
Infinite shapes of things dispersed thin;
Some such as in the world were never yet,
Nor can devised be of mortal wit;

Some daily seen, and known by their names,
Such as in idle fantasies do flit:
Infernal hags, centaurs, fiends, hippodames,[55]
apes, lions, eagles, owls, fools, lovers, children, dames.

51

And all the chamber fillèd was with flies,
Which buzzed all about, and made such sound,
That they encumbered all men's ears and eyes,
Like many swarms of bees assembled round,
After their hives with honey do abound:
All those were idle thoughts and fantasies,
Devices, dreams, opinions unsound,
Shows, visions, sooth-says, and prophesies;
And all that feigned is,[56] as leasings,[57] tales, and lies.

52

Amongst them all sat he, which woned° there,   *lived*
That hight° Phantastes by his nature true;   *was named*
A man of years yet fresh, as mote° appear,   *might*
Of swarth° complexion, and of crabbéd° hue,   *dark / gloomy*
That him full of melancholy did show;
Bent hollow beetle brows, sharp staring eyes,
That mad or foolish seemed: one by his view
Mote° deem him born with ill disposéd skies,   *might*
When oblique Saturn sat in the house of agonies.[58]

55. One source suggests these are seahorses. Maybe they're just female hippos.
56. I.e., and all that is made up.
57. I.e., "Brand new ways to improve your life! Only three easy payments of $59.99!" These are hoaxes.
58. This is a reference to the medieval view that assigned temperaments to the bodies of heaven. These in turn influenced men. Another example of this in modern language is how we might describe someone as "jovial." That's from the name Jove which was another name for Jupiter or Zeus, the king of the ancient gods. This picture of celestial influence was based upon a broadly Christian picture of the world. The universe was governed in tiers with Father, Son, and Spirit at the top and man (and creation) at the bottom, so to speak. Though various oddities sprang from this understanding, the overall picture of harmony, order, and motion fits well with a Christian cosmology. And the stars *are* angels after all (Lk. 2:13, cf. Deut. 4:19).

53

Whom Alma having showed to her guests,
Thence brought them to the second room, whose walls
Were painted fair with memorable jests,
Of famous wizards, and with pictorals°   *pictures*
Of magistrates, of courts, of tribunals,
Of commonwealths, of states, of policy,
Of laws, of judgements, and of decretals°;   *decrees*
All arts, all science, all philosophy,
And all that in the world was aye° thought wittily°.[59]   *ever / creatively*

54

Of those that room was full, and them among
There sat a man of ripe and perfect age,
Who did them meditate all his life long,
That through continual practice and usage,
He now was grown right wise, and wondrous sage.[60]
Great pleasure had those stranger knights, to see
His goodly reason, and grave personage,
That his disciples both desired to be;
But Alma thence them led to the hind most room of three.

55

That chamber seemed ruinous and old,
And therefore was removéd far behind,
Yet were the walls, that did the same uphold,
Right firm and strong, though somewhat they declined;
And therein sat an old, old man, half blind,
And all decrepit in his feeble corse°,   *body*
Yet lively vigor rested in his mind,
And recompensed him with a better source:
Weak body well is changed for mind's redoubled force.[61]

---

59. Spenser's picture of art, science, and philosophy as bound together is one we would do well to learn. Right and wrong, ugly and beautiful, natural and unnatural are all bound up together.

60. This second part of the brain is judgment, understanding, or wisdom. Take your pick.

61. This third wise man represents memory. Notice how he's old and "half blind."

56

This man of infinite remembrance was,
And things foregone through many ages held,
Which he recorded still, as they did pass,
Nor suffered them to perish through long eld,
As all things else, the which this world doth weld°,   *rule*
But laid them up in his immortal shrine,
Where they forever uncorrupted dwelled:[62]
The wars he well remembered of king Nine,
Of old Assaracus, and Inachus divine.[63]

57

The years of Nestor nothing were to his,
Nor yet Methuselah, though longest lived;
For he remembered both their infancies:
Nor wonder then, if that he were deprived
Of native strength now, that he them survived.
His chamber all was hanged about with rolls,
And old records from ancient times derived,
Some made in books, some in long parchment scrolls,
That were all worm-eaten, and full of canker holes.[64]

58

Amidst them all he in a chair was set,
Tossing and turning them without end;
But for he was unable them to fetch,
A little boy did on him still attend,

62. This old man represents the most ideal memory. He remembers everything and has forgotten nothing. His name is given at the end of section 58 as Eumnestes.

63. Remember King Nine was mentioned back in IX.22. This is the old name for the founder of Babylon/Babel, whom the Bible calls Nimrod (Gen. 10:8–10). As the first recorded attempt at human civilization, it represents the earliest days of memory. According to Greek mythology, Assaracus was the great-great grandson of Zeus, a prince of Troy, and the ancestor of Romulus and Remus, the Cain and Abel of Rome. Inachus was a river god and the king of Argos. All of these references are meant to illustrate that he has forgotten nothing, and remembers even these earliest days of human history. His mind is a steel trap.

64. This man is older and even more vigorous than Nestor, who was reputed to have gone to the Trojan War at around 110 years of age. Methusaleh of course holds the record for longest recorded life (Gen. 5:27), and yet, this old man—Eumnestes—even has him beat. And that explains why his chamber is so full of books and scrolls and why they look so old.

To reach, whenever he for ought did send;
And oft when things were lost, or laid amiss,
That boy them sought, and unto him did lend.
Therefore he Anamnestes cleppéd° is,   *called*
And that old man Eumnestes, by their properties.[65]

59

The knights there entering, did him reverence due
And wondered at his endless exercise,
Then as they 'gan his library to view,
And antique registers for to avise°,   *look at*
There chanced to the Prince's hand to rise,
An ancient book, hight° Briton Monuments,   *named*
That of this land's first conquest did devise°,   *describe*
And old division into regiments,
Till it reducéd was to one man's governments.

60

Sir Guyon chanced eke° on another book,   *also*
That hight° Antiquity of Faerie Land.   *named*
In which when as he greedily did look;
The offspring of elves and fairies there he found,
As it delivered was from hand to hand:
Where at they burning both with fervent fire,
Their countries' ancestry to understand,
Cravéd leave of Alma, and that agéd sire,
To read those books; who gladly granted their desire.[66]

65. "Anamnestes" is Greek for "remember." That's the boy who fetches things for the old man, and "Eumnestes" is Greek for "good memory." He's the old man.

66. Yeah! Books! We will learn about the books Arthur and Guyon are reading in the next canto.

o Your Worst

Directions: Identify where in the story the following quotes came from. Explain what they mean and their significance to the story.

    1. "Stern was their look, like wild amazéd stares,
        Staring with hollow eyes, and stiff upstanding hairs."

    2. "Pensive I yield I am, and sad in mind,
        Through great desire of glory and of fame:
        Nor ought I ween are ye therein behind,
        That have twelve months sought one, yet no where can her find."

    3. "And all the chamber filléd was with flies,
        Which buzzed all about, and made such sound,
        That they encumbered all men's ears and eyes,
        Like many swarms of bees assembled round."

Canto X.[1]

A chronicle of Briton kings,
from Brute to Uther's reign.
And rolls of Elfin Emperors,
till time of Gloriane.

1

Who now shall give unto me words and sound,
Equal unto this haughty enterprise?
Or who shall lend me wings, with which from ground
Lowly verse may loftily arise,
And lift itself unto the highest skies?
More ample spirit, than hitherto was wont°,   *needed*
Here needs me, whiles the famous ancestries
Of my most dreaded sovereign I recount,
By which all earthly princes she doth far surmount.[2]

---

1. Canto 10 is Spenser's retelling of the books that Arthur and Guyon are reading. The first is Arthur's book, a history of England, and Guyon's follows, a history of Faerie Land. The history of England is a mythical retelling, meaning that it is *mostly* true. If you can sit back and relax and enjoy the tales, the history does serve the purpose of the overall story. It is example after example of intemperate or temperate people. The point being that temperance is learned by knowing the past. A temperate man or woman must know how his or her ancestors failed or succeeded in their quest for the good life. This is also what Spenser promised in the introduction of this book. He said that he would tell the story of England, the Queen, and her lands. So don't get tripped up by all the details, just enjoy the ride!

2. Spenser exclaims that the subject matter he is about to relate is far higher and fairer than he has yet attempted. He is about to tell of the lineage of his "dreaded sovereign," her majesty, Queen Elizabeth I of England.

2

Nor under sun, that shines so wide and fair,
Whence all that lives, does borrow life and light,
Lives ought, that to her lineage may compare,
Which though from earth it be derivéd right,
Yet doth itself stretch forth to heaven's height,
And all the world with wonder overspread;
A labor huge, exceeding far my might:
How shall frail pen, with fear disparaged,
Conceive such sovereign glory, and great bountihead°?   *blessing-kindness*

3

Argument worthy of Moeonian³ quill,
Or rather worthy of great Phoebus' rote°,   *harp*
Whereon the ruins of great Ossa hill,
And triumphs of Phlegraean Jove he wrote,⁴
That all the gods admired his lofty note.
But if some relish of that heavenly lay°   *song*
His learnéd daughters would to me report,⁵
To deck my song withal, I would assay°,   *tell*
Thy name, O sovereign Queen, to blazon° far away.⁶   *make famous*

4

Thy name O sovereign Queen, thy realm and race,
From this renownéd Prince derivéd are,⁷
Who mightily upheld that royal mace,
Which now thou bearest, to thee descended far
From mighty kings and conquerors in war,
Thy fathers and great grandfathers of old,
Whose noble deeds above the northern star
Immortal fame for ever hath enrolled;
As in that old man's book they were in order told.

---

3. Homer used to be thought to have come from Maeonia, an ancient town in Asia Minor. Thus "Moeonian" would mean "Homeric."

4. These names refer to an incident when giants sought to climb Mt. Olympus from Mt. Ossa. They were defeated by Jove at Phlegra.

5. His daughters were the nine muses.

6. Spenser is saying that it will take the great muses of some of the greatest tales ever told in order for him to do justice to the story he is about to tell about the Queen.

7. The "Prince" is Arthur. Spenser says that the Queen (here referring to Queen Elizabeth I) is descended from him.

5

The land, which warlike Britons now possess,
And therein have their mighty empire raised,
In antique times was salvage° wilderness,   *wild*
Unpeopled, unmannered, unproved, unpraised,
Nor was it island then, nor was it pased°   *placed*
Amid the ocean waves, nor was it sought
Of merchants far, for profits therein praised,
But was all desolate, and of some thought
By sea to have been for the Celtic mainland brought.[8]

6

Nor did it then deserve a name to have,
Till that the venturous° mariner that way   *adventurous*
Learning his ship from those white rocks to save,
Which all along the southern sea-coast lay,
Threatening unheedy° wreck and rash decay,   *careless*
For safety's sake that same his sea-mark made,
And named it Albion.[9] But later day
Finding in it fit ports for fisher's trade,
'Gan more the same frequent, and further to invade.

7

But far inland a savage nation dwelt,
Of hideous giants, and half beastly men,
That never tasted grace, nor goodness felt,
But like wild beasts lurking in loathsome den,
And flying fast as roebuck through the fen°,   *marsh*
All naked without shame, or care of cold,
By hunting and by spoiling livéd then;
Of stature huge, and eke° of courage bold,   *also*
That sons of men amazed their sternness to behold.[10]

8

But whence they sprung, or how they were begot,
Uneath° is to assure°; uneath to ween°   *impossible / to be sure / believe*

8. We start with Briton when it was young, unpeopled, and uncultivated.

9. "Albion" is the old name for England. This is from the Latin 'albus' for the white-rocked coasts.

10. The earliest merchants began to fish and settle along the coasts. But little did they know, beastly giant men inhabited the inland.

That monstrous error, which doth some assot°,   *amaze*
That Dioclesian's fifty daughters sheen°   *beautiful*
Into this land by chance have driven been,
Where companing° with fiends and filthy sprites°,   *marrying / creatures*
Through vain illusion of their lust unclean,
They brought forth giants and such dreadful wights°,   *creatures*
As far exceeded men in their immeasured mights.[11]

9

They held this land, and with their filthiness
Polluted this same gentle soil long time:
That their own mother loathed their beastliness,
And 'gan abhor her brood's unkindly crime,
All were they born of her own native slime,
Until that Brutus anciently derived
From royal stock of old Assarac's line,
Driven by fatal error, here arrived,
And them of their unjust possession deprived.[12]

10

But ere° he had established his throne,   *before*
And spread his empire to the utmost shore,
He fought great battles with his savage fone°;   *foes*
In which he them defeated evermore,
And many giants left on groaning floor;
That well can witness yet unto this day
The western Hoe, besprinkled with the gore
Of mighty Göemot, whom in stout fray
Corineus conquered, and cruelly did slay.

11

And eke° that ample pit, yet far renowned,   *also*
For the large leap, which Debon did compel
Coulin to make, being eight lugs° of ground;   *rods*
Into the which returning back, he fell:

11. The origin of these beastly giant men was the marrying of fifty of Dioclesian's daughters with monsters and demons. The offspring of these marriages were giants and monsters with incredible strength and might.

12. The offspring of these marriages were despised by their mothers, but they inhabited the land until Brutus, a Roman descended from Aeneas, arrived and cleared the land of the monsters.

But those three monstrous stones do most excel
Which that huge son of hideous Albion,[13]
Whose father Hercules in France did quell,
Great Godmer threw, in fierce contention,
At bold Canutus; but of him was slain anon°.   *thereafter*

12

In meed° of these great conquests by them got,   *reward*
Corineus had that province utmost west,
To him assigned for his worthy lot,
Which of his name and memorable jest
He called Cornewaile, yet so calléd best:
And Debon's share was, that is Devonshire:
But Canute had his portion from the rest,
The which he called Canutium, for his hire°;   *reward*
Now Cantium, which Kent we commonly inquire.[14]

13

Thus Brute° this realm unto his rule subdued,   *Brutus*
And reignéd long in great felicity,
Lovéd of his friends, and of his foes eschewed°,   *avoided*
He left three sons, his famous progeny,
Born of fair Inogene of Italy;
'Mongst whom he parted his imperial state,
And Locrine left chief lord of Brittany.
At last ripe age bade him surrender late
His life, and long good fortune unto final fate.[15]

14

Locrine was left the sovereign lord of all;
But Albanact had all the northern part,
Which of himself Albania he did call;
And Camber did possess the western quart,
Which Severn now from Logris doth depart°:   *divide*
And each his portion peaceably enjoyed,
Nor was there outward breach, nor grudge in heart,

13. Albion is here referring to one giant in particular, not the ancient land of Briton.

14. Sources say that parts of this are relayed in other stories and parts seem to be relayed by Spenser alone. The point being that these men of Brutus drove back the giant race, and their names and provinces are still in Briton to this day.

15. Brutus died, leaving three sons among whom he divided his lands.

That once their quiet government annoyed,
But each his pains to others' profit still employed.[16]

15

Until a nation strange, with visage swart°,	*swarthy*
And courage fierce, that all men did affray°,	*scare*
Which through the world then swarmed in every part,	
And overflowed all countries far away,	
Like Noah's great flood, with their importune° sway,	*troublesome*
This land invaded with like violence,	
And did themselves through all the north display:	
Until that Locrine for his realm's defense,	
Did head against them make, and strong munificence°.[17]	*fortification*

16

He them encountered, a confuséd rout,	
For by the river, that whilom° was hight°	*formerly / called*
The ancient Abus, where with courage stout	
He them defeated in victorious fight,	
And chased so fiercely after fearful flight,	
That force their chieftain, for his safety's sake,	
(Their Chieftain Humber naméd was aright)	
Unto the mighty stream him to betake,	
Where he an end of battle, and of life did make.[18]	

17

The king returnéd proud of victory,	
And insolent walks through unwonted° ease,	*careless*
That shortly he forgot the jeopardy,	
Which in his land he lately did appease,	
And fell to vain voluptuous disease:	
He loved fair Lady Estrild, lewdly loved,	
Whose wanton pleasures him too much did please.	

16. His three sons were Locrine, Albanact, and Camber. Albania was in the north which is modern day Scotland. Camber's land in the west is now known as Cambria or Wales. The Severn is a river that divides Wales and England.

17. The three sons of Brutus ruled in peace for a while until a new "nation strange" began invading from the north and Locrine had to prepare his realm for defense.

18. The River Abus was named the Humber because that was the chief's name of the "nation strange" who tried to escape the battle by swimming the river, but he drowned instead.

That quite his heart from Gwendolyn removed,
For Gwendolyn his wife, though always faithful proved.[19]

18

The noble daughter of Corineus
Would not endure to be so vile disdained,
But gathering force, and courage valorous,
Encountered him in battle well ordained,
In which him vanquished she to fly constrained:
But she so fast pursued, that him she took,
And threw in bands, where he till death remained;
Also his fair leman°, flying through a brook,   *lover*
She overhent°, not moved with her piteous look.   *overtook*

19

But both herself, and eke° her daughter dear,   *also*
Begotten by her kingly paramour°,   *lover*
The fair Sabrina almost dead with fear,
She there attacked, far from all succor°;   *help*
The one she slew in that impatient stour°,   *situation*
But the sad virgin innocent of all,
A down the rolling river she did pour,
Which of her name now Severn men do call:
Such was the end, that to disloyal love did fall.[20]

20

Then for her son, which she to Locrine bore,
Madan was young, unmeet the rule of sway,
In her own hand the crown she kept in store,
Till riper years he wrought, and stronger stay:
During which time her power she did display
Through all this realm, the glory of her sex,
And first taught men a woman to obey:

19. Locrine, proud of his victories, returned and began living intemperately, being unfaithful to his wife, Gwendolyn, and loving Lady Estrild.

20. Gwendolyn is the "noble daughter of Corineus." She would not stand by and let immorality reign, and gathering an army, she attacked her husband and his forces, defeated him, and put him in prison where he lived the remainder of his days. Then she pursued his lover, Lady Estrild, and her daughter, Sabrina, born of Locrine. There, Gwendolyn killed Lady Estrild and threw Sabrina into the river where she perished.

But when her son to man's estate did wax,
She it surrendered, nor herself would longer vex.[21]

21

Then Madan reigned, unworthy of his race:
For with all shame that sacred throne he filled:
Next Memprise, as unworthy of that place,
In which being consorted with Manild,
For thirst of single kingdom him he killed.
But Ebranck saved both their infamies
With noble deeds, and warréd on Brunchild
In Henault, where yet of his victories
Brave monuments remain, which yet that land envies.[22]

22

An happy man in his first days he was,
And happy father of fair progeny:
For all so many weeks as the year has,
So many children he did multiply;[23]
Of which were twenty sons, which did apply,
Their minds to praise, and chivalrous desire:
Those germans° did subdue all Germany,   *brothers*
Of whom it hight°; but in the end their sire   *named*
With foul repulse from France was forced to retire.

23

Which blot his son succeeding in his seat,
The second Brute, the second both in name,
And eke° in semblance of his puissance° great,   *also / strength*
Right well recured°, and did away that blame   *repaired*
With recompense° of everlasting fame.[24]   *reward*
He with his victor sword first openéd,
The bowels of wide France, a forlorn dame,
And taught her first how to be conqueréd;
Since which, with sundry spoils she hath been ransackéd.

21. Gwendolyn reigned over Locrine's land until her son, Madan, was old enough to rule. Then she gave the crown to him.
22. Unfortunately Madan and Memprise, the next two rulers, were apparently pretty wicked. But Ebranck came along and saved the kingdom.
23. Wow! How many children is that?
24. Ebranck's successor was Brutus II. He was "the second" in name and in deed.

24

Let Scaldis tell, and let tell Hania,
And let the marsh of Estham Bruges tell,
What color were their waters that same day,
And all the moor twixt Elversham and Dell,
With blood of Henalois, which therein fell.
How oft that day did sad Brunchildis see
The green shield dyed in dolorous° vermeil°?   *sad / red*
That not *Scuith guiridh*[25] it mote° seem to be   *might*
But rather *y Scuith gogh*,[26] sign of sad cruelty.[27]

25

His son King Leill by father's labor long,
Enjoyed an heritage of lasting peace,
And built Cairleill, and built Cairleon strong.
Next Huddibras his realm did not increase,
But taught the land from weary wars to cease.
Whose footsteps Bladud following in arts
Excelled at Athens all the learnéd press,
From whence he brought them to these savage parts,
And with sweet science mollified° their stubborn hearts.[28]   *satisfied*

26

Ensample° of his wondrous faculty,   *example*
Behold the boiling baths at Cairbadon,
Which seethe with secret fire eternally,
And in their entrails, full of quick brimstone,
Nourish the flames, which they are warmed upon,
That to their people wealth they forth do well,
And health to every foreign nation:
Yet he at last contending to excel
The reach of men, through flight into fond° mischief fell.[29]   *immoderate*

27

Next him King Lear[30] in happy peace long reigned,
But had no issue male him to succeed,

---

25. Welsh: green shield
26. Welsh: red shield
27. Brutus II fought many battles and turned many green shields to red.
28. The next few rulers enjoyed peace and began to study arts and wisdom.
29. This probably means that he tried to fly, like the Wright Brothers, and he failed and died.
30. King Lear is famous for the play Shakespeare wrote with the title.

But three fair daughters, which were well untrained,
In all that seemed fit for kingly seed:
'Mongst whom his realm he equally decreed
To have divided. Though when feeble age
Nigh to his utmost date he saw proceed,
He called his daughters; and with speeches sage
Inquired, which of them most did love her parentage.

28

The eldest Gonorill 'gan to protest,
That she much more than her own life him loved:
And Regan greater love to him professed,
Than all the world, when ever it were proved;
But Cordeill said she loved him, as behooved:
Whose simple answer, wanting colors fair
To paint it forth, him to displeasance° moved,   *displeasure*
That in his crown he counted her no heir,
But twixt the other twain his kingdom whole did share.[31]

29

So wedded the one to Maglan king of Scots,
And the other to the king of Cambria,
And twixt them shared his realm by equal lots:
But without dower[32] the wise Cordelia
Was sent to Aganip of Celtica.
Their agéd sire, thus eased of his crown,
A private life led in Albania,
With Gonorill, long had in great renown,
That naught him grieved to been from rule deposéd down.

30

But true it is, that when the oil is spent,
The light goes out, and wick is thrown away;
So when he had resigned his regiment,

31. King Lear decides to divide his kingdom among his three daughters, and to see who will get what, he asks them who loves him the most. Brilliant scheme. Anyhow, the first two, Gonorill (great name) and Regan, slobber and drool all over their father promising the greatest loves. Cordeill, however, answered simply that she loved her father as a daughter ought to. This response did not please her father, and she was disinherited.

32. A "dower" is like a dowry—a gift of money or property that a bride brings into a marriage, or simply an inheritance as in this case. Cordeill (or Cordelia) received no inheritance and was sent to Celtica.

His daughter 'gan despise his drooping day,
And weary wax° of his continual stay.   *grow*
Then to his daughter Regan he repaired°,   *went*
Who him at first well used every way;
But when of his departure she despaired,
Her bounty she abated, and his cheer impaired.[33]

31

The wretched man 'gan then avise° too late,   *realize*
That love is not, where most it is professed,
Too truly tried in his extremist state;
At last resolved likewise to prove the rest,
He to Cordelia himself addressed,
Who with entire affection him received,
As for her sire and king her seemed best;
And after all an army strong she leaved°,   *raised*
To war on those, which him had of his realm bereaved.[34]

32

So to his crown she him restored again,
In which he died, made ripe for death by eld,[35]
And after willed, it should to her remain:
Who peaceably the same long time did wield:
And all men's hearts in due obedience held:
Till that her sister's children, waxen strong
Through proud ambition, against her rebelled,
And overcoming kept in prison long,[36]
Till weary of that wretched life, herself she hung.[37]

33. The wicked daughters hope their dad will soon die.

34. King Lear in the end realized that he was most loved by Cordelia, even though she professed such a simple love. She helped raise an army and they pursued the other daughters and their husbands who had torn the kingdom from him.

35. That "eld" is an abbreviation for "elder ones" referring to the older daughters of the king.

36. Cordelia ruled for many years until the sons of her older sisters rebelled and took the kingdom back. Thereafter she spent many years in prison.

37. So much for "wise." Cordelia hung herself after spending a long time in jail. Although the Greeks saw some kind "honor" in suicide, murder is always cowardly. Murder of another or of one's self is always out of fear of the wrong thing(s). We are called to fear God and fight with courage, scorning death, until God relieves us of duty. Until then, no matter the difficulty, life is our noble pursuit.

33

Then 'gan the bloody brethren both to reign:
But fierce Cundah 'gan shortly to envy
His brother Morgan, pricked with proud disdain,
To have a peer in part of sovereignty,
And kindling coals of cruel enmity,
Raised war, and him in battle overthrew:
Whence as he to those woody hills did fly,
Which hight° of him Glamorgan, there him slew: *called*
Then did he reign alone, when he none equal knew.[38]

34

His son Rivallo his dead room did supply,
In whose sad time blood did from heaven rain:
Next great Gurgustus, then fair Caecily
In constant peace their kingdoms did contain,
After whom Lago, and Kinmark did reign,
And Gorbogud, till far in years he grew:
Then his ambitious sons unto them twain
Arraught° the rule, and from their father drew,   *took over*
Stout Ferrex and stern Porrex him in prison threw.

35

But O, the greedy thirst of royal crown,
That knows no kindred, nor regards no right,
Stirred Porrex up to put his brother down;
Who unto him assembling foreign might,
Made war on him, and fell himself in fight:
Whose death to avenge, his mother merciless,
Most merciless of women, Wyden hight°,   *named*
Her other son fast sleeping did oppress,
And with most cruél hand him murdered pitiless.[39]

36

Here ended Brutus' sacred progeny,
Which had seven hundred years this scepter born,
With high renown, and great felicity?

38. Cundah, one of the older sisters' sons, slew his brother Morgan because he wanted the whole kingdom to himself. "Gimme, gimme," he said.

39. So the two sons threw their father into prison, turned on each other and went to war, leaving one alive, and then his mom (apparently feeling a bit left out) killed him. What a happy little family.

The noble branch from the antique stock was torn
Through discord, and the royal throne forlorn:
Thenceforth this realm was into factions rent,
Whilst each of Brutus boasted to be born,
That in the end was left no monument
Of Brutus, nor of Briton's glory ancient.[40]

37

Then up arose a man of matchless might,
And wondrous wit to manage high affairs,
Who stirred with pity of the stresséd plight
Of this sad realm, cut into sundry shares
By such, as claimed themselves Brut's rightful heirs,
Gathered the princes of the people loose,
To taken counsel of their common cares;
Who with his wisdom won, him straight did choose
Their king, and swore him fealty to win or loose.

38

Then made he head against his enemies,
And Ymner slew, of Logris[41] miscreate°;   *wrongful ruler*
Then Ruddoc and proud Stater, both allies,
This of Albany newly nominate,
And that of Cambry king confirméd late,
He overthrew through his own valiance;
Whose countries he reduced to quiet state,
And shortly brought to civil governance,
Now one, which earst° were many, made through variance.   *before*

39

Then made he sacred laws, which some men say
Were unto him revealed in vision,
By which he freed the traveler's highway,
The Church's part, and ploughman's portion,
Restraining stealth, and strong extortion;
The gracious Numa of great Brittany:
For till his days, the chief dominion
By strength was wielded without policy;
Therefore he first wore crown of gold for dignity.

40. And with that, the line of Brutus is done. It's probably for the best.
41. Logris is England. Remember that's the province that Locrine ruled.

40

Donwallo died (for what may live for aye°?)[42]   *forever*
And left two sons, of peerless prowess both;
That sackéd Rome too dearly did assay°,   *under go*
The recompense of their perjured oath,
And ransacked Greece well tried, when they were wroth°;   *angry*
Besides subjected France, and Germany,
Which yet their praises speak, all be they loth°,   *honor*
And inly° tremble at the memory   *inwardly*
Of Brennus and Bellinus, kings of Brittany.

41

Next them did Gurgunt, great Bellinus' son
In rule succeed, and eke° in father's praise;   *also*
He Easterland subdued, and Denmark won,
And of them both did foy° and tribute raise,   *faith*
The which was due in his dead father's days:
He also gave to fugitives of Spain,
Whom he at sea found wandering from their ways,
A seat in Ireland safely to remain,
Which they should hold of him, as subject to Britain.

42

After him reigned Guitheline his heir,
The justest man and truest in his days,
Who had to wife Dame Mertia the fair,
A woman worthy of immortal praise,
Which for this realm found many goodly lays°,   *laws*
And wholesome statutes to her husband brought;
Her many deemed to have been of the fays°,   *elves*
As was Aegerie, that Numa taught;
Those yet of her be Mertian laws both named and thought.[43]

42. Notice how Spenser talks about this guy for several stanzas before revealing his name. Talk about suspenseful. Ah-ha! It's Donwallo! The first English king to wear a crown of gold! He united England and made many wise laws (like Numa did in Italy) to keep peace and govern the land.

43. The Lady Mertia, Guitheline's wife, gave him many wise counsels and laws. This and the preceding stanzas picture a kind of "Solomonic" period in England's history. The kings have sway over the nations, tribute is brought from far and near, and Lady Wisdom (Dame Mertia) reigns at the right hand of the king.

43

Her son Sisillus after her did reign,
And then Kimarus, and then Danius;
Next whom Morindus did the crown sustain,
Who, had he not with wrath outrageous,
And cruél rancor° dimmed his valorous   *bitterness*
And mighty deeds, should matchéd have the best:
As well in that same field victorious
Against the foreign Morands he expressed;
Yet lives his memory, though carcass sleep in rest.

44

Five sons he left begotten of one wife,
All which successively by turns did reign;
First Gorboman a man of virtuous life;
Next Archigald, who for his proud disdain,
Deposed was from princedom sovereign,
And piteous Elidure put in his stead;
Who shortly it to him restored again,
Till by his death he it recoveréd;
But Peridure and Vigent him disthronized.[44]

45

In wretched prison long he did remain,
Till they out-reignéd had their utmost date,
And then therein re-seizéd was again,
And ruléd long with honorable state,
Till he surrendered realm and life to fate.
Then all the sons of these five brethren reigned
By due success, and all their nephews late°,   *after*
Even thrice eleven descents the crown retained,
Till agéd Hely by due heritage it gained.[45]

46

He had two sons, whose eldest called Lud
Left of his life most famous memory,
And endless monuments of his great good:

44. You can figure it out. He got kicked off the throne. You should read that stanza several times. It's pretty goofy.

45. Mr. Hely came to the throne after thirty-three descendents of the five fighting brothers.

The ruined walls he did re-edify°   *rebuild*
Of Troynovant,[46] 'gainst force of enemy,
And built that gate, which of his name is hight°,   *called*
By which he lies entombéd solemnly.
He left two sons, too young to rule aright,
Androgeus and Tenantius, pictures of his might.

47

Whilst they were young, Cassibalane their eme°   *uncle*
Was by the people chosen in their stead,
Who on him took the royal diadem,
And goodly well long time it governéd,
Till the proud Romans him disquietéd,
And warlike Caesar, tempted with the name
Of this sweet island, never conqueréd,
And envying the Briton's blazéd fame,
(O hideous hunger of dominion) hither came.[47]

48

Yet twice they were repulsed back again,
And twice reinforced, back to their ships to fly,
The whiles with blood they all the shore did stain,
And the gray ocean into purple dye:
Nor had they footing found at last perdie°,   *in fact*
Had not Androgeus, false to native soil,
And envious of uncle's sovereignty,
Betrayed his country unto foreign spoil:
Naught else, but treason, from the first this lad did foil°.   *plot*

49

So by him Caesar got the victory,
Through great bloodshed, and many a sad assay°,   *event*
In which himself was chargéd heavily
Of hardy Nennius, whom he yet did slay,
But lost his sword, yet to be seen this day.
Thenceforth this land was tributary made
To ambitious Rome, and did their rule obey,

46. That's the old school name for London.
47. Spenser has now reached the point in England's history where the Romans are trying to conquer it.

Till Arthur all that reckoning did defray°;   *settle*
Yet oft the Briton kings against them strongly swayed°.[48]   *fought*

50

Next him Tenantius reigned, then Kimbeline,
What time the eternal Lord in fleshly slime
Enwombéd was, from wretched Adam's line
To purge away the guilt of sinful crime:
O joyous memory of happy time,
That heavenly grace so plenteously displayéd;
(O too high ditty for my simple rhyme.)
Soon after this the Romans him warréd;
For that their tribute he refused to let be paid.[49]

51

Good Claudius, that next was emperor,
An army brought, and with him battle fought,
In which the king was by a treachetour°   *traitor*
Disguiséd slain, ere° any thereof thought: *before*
Yet ceaséd not the bloody fight for ought;
For Arvirage his brother's place supplied,
Both in his arms, and crown, and by that draught
Did drive the Romans to the weaker side,
That they to peace agreed. So all was pacified.[50]

52

Was never king more highly magnified,
Nor dread of Romans, then was Arvirage,
For which the emperor to him allied
His daughter Genuiss' in marriage:
Yet shortly he renounced the vassalage°   *servitude*

48. Briton finally fell to the Romans when Androgeus betrayed them. And though they were subdued they continued to fight until they were finally delivered by Arthur.

49. This event gives us our anchor in time. Spenser, like all astute historians, sees the center of history in the Incarnation, when the "eternal Lord in fleshly slime enwombéd was." It doesn't seem to be any accident that this stanza is structured the way it is. Kimbeline's rule is mentioned in the first and last lines, emphasizing the *centrality* of the Incarnation, but also giving reason for and defending the actions of Kimbeline. The Incarnation is about paying the debt of sin and freeing us from its bondage. Likewise, Kimbeline refused to pay tribute to pagan (Roman) powers.

50. This is remembered in history as The Great Pacifier War. Maybe?

Of Rome again, who hither hastily sent
Vespasian, that with great spoil and rage
Forwasted° all, till Genuissa gent°   *wasted / gentleman*
Persuaded him to cease, and her lord to relent.[51]

53

He died; and him succeeded Marius,
Who joyed his days in great tranquillity,
Then Coyll, and after him good Lucius,
That first received Christianity,
The sacred pledge of Christ's Evangely°;   *gospel*
Yet true it is, that long before that day
Hither came Joseph of Arimathy,[52]
Who brought with him the holy grail,[53] (they say)
And preached the truth, but since it greatly did decay.[54]

54

This good king shortly without issue° died,   *children*
Whereof great trouble in the kingdom grew,
That did herself in sundry° parts divide,   *various*
And with her power her own self overthrew,
Whilst Romans daily did the weak subdue:
Which seeing stout Bunduca, up arose,
And taking arms, the Britons to her drew;
With whom she marched straight against her foes,
And them unwares besides the Severn did enclose.

55

There she with them a cruél battle tried,
Not with so good success, as she deserved;
By reason that the captains on her side,

51. The Romans were pretty impressed with Arvirage, and the emperor gave him his daughter as a token of their peace. Of course this was quickly broken and the two nations were at war once more, but it was the wife/daughter, Genuissa, who was able to break up the fight. Another Medina.

52. See Mark 15:43 and John 19:38 for more on Joseph of Arimathea. He was the disciple who took Jesus' body down from the cross and placed it in the tomb.

53. The Holy Grail was believed to be the cup that Christ drank from at the Last Supper. It's whereabouts have been the subject of many chivalrous and not so chivalrous undertakings.

54. The gospel had been preached by Joseph of Arimathea, says Spenser, but it had slowly been forgotten until the time of Lucius.

Corrupted by Paulinus, from her swerved:
Yet such, as were through former flight preserved,
Gathering again, her host she did renew,
And with fresh courage on the victor served:
But being all defeated, save a few,
Rather than fly, or be captivéd herself she slew.[55]

56

O famous monument of women's praise,
Matchable either to Semiramis,
Whom antique history so high doth raise,
Or to Hypsiphil' or to Thomiris:
Her host two hundred thousand numbered is;
Who whiles good fortune favoréd her might,
Triumphéd oft against her enemies;
And yet though overcome in hapless fight,
She triumphéd on death, in enemy's despite.[56]

57

Her relics° Fulgent having gathered,   *loyal followers*
Fought with Severus, and him overthrew;
Yet in the chase was slain of them, that fled:
So made them victors, whom he did subdue.
Then 'gan Carausius tyrannize anew,
And 'gainst the Romans bent their proper power,
But him Allectus treacherously slew,
And took on him the robe of emperor:
Nathless° the same enjoyed but short happy hour: *nevertheless*

58

For Asclepiodate him overcame,
And left inglorious on the vanquished plain,
Without or robe, or rag, to hide his shame.
Then afterwards he in his stead did reign;
But shortly was by Coyll in battle slain:
Who after long debate, since Lucy's time,
Was of the Britons first crowned sovereign:

55. Bunduca, a sort of proto-Joan of Arc, rose up to defend old Briton from her enemies. But her glory was short lived, and rather than face her enemies she killed herself.

56. Again, Spenser seems to think a bit too highly of suicide. The great examples we have of such action are King Saul and Judas Iscariot. If that's noble then I'm a toad.

Then 'gan this realm renew her passéd prime:
He of his name Coylchester built of stone and lime.

59

Which when the Romans heard, they hither sent
Constantius, a man of mickle° might,   *great*
With whom King Coyll made an agreement,
And to him gave for wife his daughter bright,
Fair Helena, the fairest living wight°;   *creature*
Who in all godly thews°, and goodly praise   *virtues*
Did far excel, but was most famous hight°   *called*
For skill in music of all in her days,
As well in curious instruments, as cunning lays.

60

Of whom he did great Constantine beget,[57]
Who afterward was emperor of Rome;
To which whiles absent he his mind did set,
Octavius here leapt into his room,
And it usurped by unrighteous doom:
But he his title justified by might,
Slaying Traherne, and having overcome
The Roman legion in dreadful fight:
So settled he his kingdom, and confirmed his right.

61

But wanting issue° male, his daughter dear   *offspring*
He gave in wedlock to Maximian,
And him with her made of his kingdom heir,
Who soon by means thereof the empire won,
Till murdered by the friends of Gratian;
Then 'gan the Huns and Picts invade this land,
During the reign of Maximinian°;   *Maximian*
Who dying left none heir them to withstand,
But that they overran all parts with easy hand.

57. Constantine was the first Christian emperor of the Roman Empire. He legalized
Christianity, sought the reconciliation of the Church in the midst of the Arian contro-
versy, and helped defend orthodoxy at the Council of Nicea.

62

The weary Britons, whose war-able youth
Was by Maximian lately led away,
With wretched miseries, and woeful ruth°,   *pity*
Were to those pagans made an open prey,
And daily spectacle of sad decay:
Whom Roman wars, which now four hundred years,
And more had wasted, could no whit° dismay;   *bit*
Till by consent of commons and of peers,
They crowned the second Constantine with joyous tears,

63

Who having oft in battle vanquishéd
Those spoilful Picts, and swarming Easterlings,
Long time in peace his realm establishéd,
Yet oft annoyed with sundry bordragings°   *border raids*
Of neighbor Scots, and foreign scatterlings°,   *raiders*
With which the world did in those days abound:
Which to outbar°, with painful pionings[58]   *keep out*
From sea to sea he heaped a mighty mound,
Which from Alcluid to Panwelt did that border bound.

64

Three sons he dying left, all under age;
By means whereof, their uncle Vortigere
Usurped the crown, during their pupilage;
Which the infants' tutors gathering to fear,
Them closely into Armorick did bear:
For dread of whom, and for those Picts annoys,
He sent to Germany, strange aid to rear,
From whence eftsoones° arrivéd here three hoys[59]   *again*
Of Saxons, whom he for his safety employs.

65

Two brethren were their captains, which hight°   *called*
Hengist and Horsus, well approved in war,
And both of them men of renownéd might;

58. He dug this sizeable earthen wall, so "pionings" are apparently "diggings." Although for what it's worth, a "pion" is a sub-atomic particle. Perhaps Spenser is suggesting early advances in chemistry.
59. "Hoys" are small ships, from whence we get the "Ahoy there, mate!"

Who making vantage of their civil jar,
And of those foreigners, which came from far,
Grew great, and got large portions of land,
That in the realm ere° long they stronger are,   *before*
Then they which sought at first their helping hand,
And Vortiger enforced the kingdom to aband°.[60]   *abandon*

66

But by the help of Vortimere his son,
He is again unto his rule restored,
And Hengist seeming sad, for that was done,
Receivéd is to grace and new accord,
Through his fair daughters face, and flattering word;
Soon after which, three hundred lords he slew
Of British blood, all sitting at his board;
Whose doleful monuments who list° to rue°,   *wish / pity*
The eternal marks of treason may at Stonehenge view.[61]

67

By this the sons of Constantine, which fled,
Ambrose and Uther did ripe years attain,
And here arriving, strongly challenged
The crown, which Vortiger did long detain:
Who flying from his guilt, by them was slain,
And Hengist eke° soon brought to shameful death.   *also*
Thenceforth Aurelius peaceably did reign,
Till that through poison stoppéd was his breath;
So now entombéd lies at Stonehenge by the heath.[62]

60. The first Saxons were these two brothers, Hengist and Horsus.

61. Stonehenge is the circular assembly of gigantic stones believed to have been related to some sort of cultic worship at some point. However the legends contest that they were set up by the wizard Merlin as a memorial to these slain nobles. For myself, I'm inclined to believe that they're an ancient set of dominoes that a race of giants forgot to put away.

62. "Heath" refers to a hillock or moor of land. While it isn't so important to the story to keep track of *exactly* what's going on, it is important to notice how power and greed easily corrupt. Ruler after ruler is killed by another seeking to sit in his place. There are very few who enjoy peaceful reigns. Temperance giveth life; intemperance taketh it away.

68

After him Uther, which Pendragon hight°,   *called*
Succeeding... There abruptly it did end,
Without full point, or other ceasure° right,   *ending*
As if the rest some wicked hand did rend,
Or the author self could not at least attend
To finish it: that so untimely breach
The Prince himself half seemeth to offend,
Yet secret pleasure did offence impeach,
And wonder of antiquity long stopped his speech.[63]

69

At last quite ravished with delight, to hear
The royal offspring of his native land,
Cried out, "Dear country, O how dearly dear
Ought thy remembrance, and perpetual band°   *bond*
Be to thy foster child, that from thy hand
Did common breath and nurture receive?
How brutish is it not to understand,
How much to her we owe, that all us gave,
That gave unto us all, whatever good we have."

70

But Guyon all this while his book did read,
Nor yet has ended: for it was a great[64]
And ample volume, that doth far exceed
My leisure, so long leaves here to repeat:
It told, how first Prometheus did create
A man, of many parts from beasts derived,
And then stole fire from heaven, to animate
His work, for which he was by Jove deprived
Of life himself, and heart-strings of an eagle rived.[65]

63. The Prince's book ended suddenly as though someone had been dragged away from the book mid-sentence. But Spenser is having a little fun here. Notice that the last name mentioned is Uther Pendragon, who is none other than the father of Prince Arthur. No wonder the Prince has a "secret pleasure" about this odd ending.

64. Meanwhile, Guyon has also been reading a book. This one is a history of Faerie Land.

65. Rived means "torn out." This history records that Prometheus created the first man from different parts of beasts. He then stole fire from heaven, and for doing so, was punished by Jove.

71

That man so made, he calléd Elf, to weet°   *namely*
Quick, the first author of all Elfin kind:[66]
Who wandering through the world with weary feet,
Did in the Gardens of Adonis find
A goodly creature, whom he deemed in mind
To be no earthly wight°, but either sprite°,   *creature / spirit*
Or angel, the author of all woman kind;
Therefore a fay° he her according hight°,   *faerie / called*
Of whom all faeries spring, and fetch their lineage right.[67]

72

Of these a mighty people shortly grew,
And puissant° kings, which all the world warred,   *mighty*
And to themselves all nations did subdue:
The first and eldest, which that scepter swayed,
Was Elfin; him all India obeyed,
And all that now America men call:
Next him was noble Elfinan, who laid
Cleopolis foundation first of all:
But Elfiline enclosed it with a golden wall.

73

His son was Elfinell, who overcame
The wicked goblins in bloody field:
But Elfant was of most renownéd fame,[68]
Who all of crystal did Panthea build:
Then Elfar, who two brethren giants killed,
The one of which had two heads, the other three:
Then Elfinor, who was in magic skilled;
He built by art upon the glassy sea
A bridge of brass, whose sound heaven's thunder seemed to be.[69]

66. This man was named Elf Quick. Quick means "alive" or "living thing."
67. So Mr. Quick met Ms. Fay and these were the first parents of all elves and faeries. They met, you will notice, in the Gardens of Adonis. This reminds us of Adam and Eve in the Garden of Eden, and so it is—in a manner of speaking.
68. He was renowned for his large and muscular nose. Oh wait, never mind.
69. The history of Faerie Land is strangely similar to the history of England that Arthur was just reading. Do you notice many similarities?

74

He left three sons, the which in order reigned,
And all their offspring, in their due descents,
Even seven hundred princes, which maintained
With mighty deeds their sundry° governments;   *various*
That were too long their infinite contents
Here to record, nor much material:
Yet should they be most famous monuments,
And brave ensample, both of martial°,   *warlike*
And civil rule to kings and states imperial.

75

After all these Elficleos did reign,
The wise Elficleos in great majesty,
Who mightily that scepter did sustain,
And with rich spoils and famous victory,
Did high advance the crown of Faerie:
He left two sons, of which fair Elferon
The eldest brother did untimely die;
Whose empty place the mighty Oberon
Doubly supplied, in spousal,[70] and dominion.

76

Great was his power and glory over all,
Which him before, that sacred seat did fill,
That yet remains his wide memorial:
He dying left the fairest Tanaquill,
Him to succeed therein, by his last will:
Fairer and nobler liveth none this hour,
Nor like in grace, nor like in learned skill;
Therefore they Glorian call that glorious flower,
Long mayest thou Glorian live, in glory and great power.[71]

70. That means he married his brother's widow.
71. Tanaquill is Elizabeth I, the queen of England, and she is called Gloriana as queen of Faerie Land. This ending brings the two histories "together." Spenser weaves these "histories" together for obvious purpose—Faerie Land isn't simply an imaginary land. Rather, from his point of view, it's simply a different perspective, another way of looking at the same events and people.

77

Beguiled thus with delight of novelties,
And natural desire of country's state,
So long they read in those antiquities,
That how the time was fled, they quite forgot,
Till gentle Alma seeing it so late,
Perforce their studies broke, and them besought
To think, how supper did them long await.
So half-unwilling from their books them brought,
And fairly feasted, as so noble knights she ought.[72]

72. Finally, when it has grown quite late, Alma comes and rouses the gentlemen from their study and escorts them to a feast.

You're History

Directions: Identify where in the story the following quotes came from. Explain what they mean and their significance to the story.

1. "The wretched man 'gan then avise too late,
   That love is not, where most it is professed."

2. "What time the eternal Lord in fleshly slime
   Enwombéd was, from wretched Adam's line
   To purge away the guilt of sinful crime:
   O joyous memory of happy time."

3. "That man so made, he calléd Elf, to weet
   Quick, the first author of all Elfin kind."

Canto XI.

1

What war so cruel, or what siege so sore,
As that, which strong affections do apply
Against the fort of reason evermore
Bring the soul into captivity:
Their force is fiercer through infirmity
Of the frail flesh, relenting to their rage,
And exercise most bitter tyranny
Upon the parts, brought into their bondage:
No wretchedness is like to sinful villeinage°.   *villainy*

2

But in a body, which doth freely yield
His parts to reason's rule obedient,
And letteth her that ought the scepter wield,
All happy peace and goodly government
Is settled there in sure establishment;
There Alma like a virgin queen most bright,
Doth flourish in all beauty excellent:

And to her guests doth bounteous banquet dight°,   *prepare*
Attempered goodly well for health and for delight.[1]

3

Early before the morn° with crimson ray,   *morning*
The windows of bright heaven opened had,
Through which into the world the dawning day
Might look, that maketh every creature glad,
Up rose Sir Guyon, in bright armor clad,
And to his purposed journey him prepared:
With him the Palmer eke° in habit° sad,[2]   *also / clothing*
Himself addressed to that adventure hard:
So to the river's side they both together fared.

4

Where them awaited ready at the ford
The Ferriman, as Alma had behight°,   *told*
With his well-riggéd boat: They go a board,
And he eftsoones° 'gan launch his bark° forthright.   *presently / boat*
Ere° long they rowéd were quite out of sight,   *before*
And fast the land behind them fled away.
But let them pass, whiles wind and weather right
Do serve their turns: here I a while must stay,
To see a cruél fight done by the Prince this day.[3]

5

For all so soon, as Guyon thence was gone
Upon his voyage with his trusty guide,[4]
That wicked band of villains fresh began
That castle to assail on every side,
And lay strong siege about it far and wide.

1. Remember that Alma means "soul" in Italian and "virgin" in Hebrew. Thus Alma is the "reason" that rules the castle of the body. Alma sets a good table for her guests and fills up their tummies. This refers both to the story where Alma is the hostess of Arthur and Guyon, and it refers to the body in general, where a temperate soul gives joy and health to the bones.

2. Not sad like crying, but sad like serious. The Palmer wears a black robe.

3. Spenser says that Guyon and the Palmer set sail with the Ferriman, but he leaves them there for a time because he needs to relate the following events of Prince Arthur's "cruel fight."

4. His guide is of course the Palmer with the "sad habit."

So huge and infinite their numbers were,
That all the land they under them did hide;
So foul and ugly, that exceeding fear
Their visages impressed, when they approachéd near.[5]

6

Them in twelve troops their captain did dispart°   *divide*
And round about in fittest steads° did place,   *places*
Where each might best offend his proper part,
And his contrary object most deface,
As every one seemed meetest° in that case.   *best*
Seven of the same against the castle gate,[6]
In strong entrenchments° he did closely place,   *fortifications*
Which with incessant force and endless hate,
They battered day and night, and entrance did await.

7

The other five, five sundry° ways he set,   *different*
Against the five great bulwarks of that pile°,   *castle*
And unto each a bulwark did arret°,   *line up*
To assail with open force or hidden guile,
In hope thereof to win victorious spoil.
They all that charge did fervently apply,
With greedy malice and importune toil,
And planted there their huge artillery,
With which they daily made most dreadful battery.[7]

8

The first troop was a monstrous rabblement
Of foul misshapen wights°, of which some were   *creatures*
Headed like owls, with beaks uncomely bent,
Others like dogs, others like griffins[8] drear,
And some had wings, and some had claws to tear,

5. All those ugly monster-men they had defeated the day before come back for more. Only this time there's more of them.

6. The seven troops probably represent the seven deadly sins raging war against us: anger, covetousness, envy, lust, gluttony, pride, and sloth. These seven are said to attack "the castle gate." The other five will make precision strikes. These seven, however, are the parents of all sin. Therefore they and their offspring will still be found in the other battalions.

7. These other five troops are assailing the five senses of man. Read on.

8. This creature has the body of a lion and the head and wings of an eagle.

And every one of them had lynx's eyes,
And every one did bow and arrows bear:
All those were lawless lusts, corrupt envies,
And covetous aspects, all cruél enemies.

9

Those same against the bulwark of the sight[9]
Did lay strong siege, and battelous assault,
Nor once did yield it respite° day nor night,   *rest*
But soon as Titan 'gan his head exalt,
And soon again as he his light with halt,
Their wicked engines they against it bent:
That is each thing, by which the eyes may fault:
But two than all more huge and violent,
Beauty, and money, they that bulwark sorely rent.

10

The second bulwark was the hearing sense,
'Gainst which the second troop designment° makes;   *assault*
Deforméd creatures, in strange difference,
Some having heads like harts°, some like to snakes,   *deer*
Some like wild boars late roused out of the brakes°;   *thickets*
Slanderous reproaches, and foul infamies,
Leasings, back-bitings, and vain-glorious cracks,
Bad counsels, praises, and false flatteries.
All those against that fort did bend their batteries.[10]

11

Likewise that same third fort, that is the smell
Of that third troop was cruelly assayed°:   *attacked*
Whose hideous shapes were like to fiends of hell,
Some like to hounds, some like to apes, dismayed,
Some like to puttocks°, all in plumes arrayed: *birds of prey*
All shaped according their conditions,
For by those ugly forms were portrayed,

9. This band of enemies is ugly and deformed. They represent different kinds of lusts, envies, and covetousness. And they are battling the sense of sight.

10. The second fort is the sense of hearing. Here the armies of pride, anger, and wicked words assail the walls. Spenser wisely connects the sin of pride with the sense of hearing. Pride loves to hear itself speak, and it loves to hear others speak our praises. Anger also wars on this sense. When our pride is hurt, we often respond with sharp words and lethal attacks.

Foolish delights and fond abusions°,   *abuses*
Which do that sense besiege with light illusions.[11]

                                    12
And that fourth band, which cruel battery bent,
Against the fourth bulwark, that is the taste,
Was as the rest, a greasy rabblement°,   *mob*
Some mouthed like greedy ostriches, some fast
Like loathly toads, some fashioned in the waste
Like swine; for so deformed is luxury,
Surfeit°, misdiet,[12] and unthrifty waste,   *surplus*
Vain feasts, and idle superfluity°:   *luxuries*
All those this sense's fort assail incessantly.[13]

                                    13
But the fifth troop most horrible of hue,
And fierce of force, was dreadful to report:
For some like snails, some did like spiders show,
And some like ugly urchins thick and short:
Cruelly they assailed that fifth fort,
Armed with darts of sensual delight,
With stings of carnal lust, and strong effort
Of feeling pleasures, with which day and night
Against that same fifth bulwark they continued fight.[14]

11. Here the enemy is the troop of "foolish delights and fond abusions." These sins seem to be related to slothfulness. Laziness is not simply doing nothing, though it certainly can be that. Sloth is also spending time foolishly. Delighting ourselves in things that are empty and in the end self-destructive. Spenser lines these armies up with the fort of smell, showing how the "aroma" of something is a useful gauge of its goodness or rottenness.

12. "Mis-diet" is over- or undereating, both of which continue to pummel, in turn, the modern masses. Here, Spenser is emphasizing "surplus sins," but the other end of the spectrum afflicts us with no less front. Although diet and other salvation-by-undereating techniques are all the rage in respectable circles at the present, true gratitude makes fat souls and able bodies.

13. The offspring of gluttony take their shots at the sense of taste. Notice that gluttony is not just related to diet, but rather an entire world of misuse and overuse. Spending too much money, too much food, too much time, and too much waste: all assault this fort.

14. The last fort is the sense of touch. This defense is attacked by the armies of lust and illicit bodily pleasures.

14

Thus these twelve troops with dreadful puissance°   *might*
Against that castle restless siege did lay,
And evermore their hideous ordinance
Upon the bulwarks cruélly did play,
That now it 'gan to threaten near decay:
And evermore their wicked captain
Provoked them the breaches to assay°,   *assault*
Sometimes with threats, sometimes with hope of gain,
Which by the ransack of that piece they should attain.[15]

15

On the other side, the assieged castle's ward°   *guard*
Their steadfast stands did mightily maintain,
And many bold repulse, and many hard
Achievement wrought with peril and with pain,
That goodly frame from ruin to sustain:
And those two brethren giants did defend
The walls so stoutly with their sturdy main,
That never entrance any durst pretend,
But they to direful death their groaning ghosts did send.

16

The noble virgin, lady of the place,
Was much dismayed with that dreadful sight:
For never was she in so evil case,
Till that the Prince seeing her woeful plight,
'Gan her recomfort from so sad affright°,   *fear*
Offering his service, and his dearest life
For her defense, against that carl° to fight,   *villain*
Which was their chief and the author of that strife:
She him remercied° as the patron° of her life.   *thanked / protector*

17

Eftsoones° himself in glitterand arms he dight°,   *presently / dressed*
And his well provéd weapons to him hent°;   *took*

15. Notice that each of these senses is a defense against these attacks. Often we think of the senses as merely temptations and weaknesses. But Spenser shows that with temperance, they are our strengths. Nevertheless, they are not enough on their own. These defenses will be breached if that is all we have to defend ourselves as happens here. The forts are beginning to fall—who will save the day?

So taking courteous conge[16] he behight°,   *ordered*
Those gates to be unbarred, and forth he went.
Fair mote he thee, the prowest° and most gent°,   *most courageous / noble*
That ever brandished bright steel on high:
Whom soon as that unruly rabblement°,   *mob*
With his gay Squire issuing did espy°,   *see*
They reared a most outrageous dreadful yelling cry,

18
And therewith all at once at him let fly[17]
Their fluttering arrows, thick as flakes of snow,[18]
And round about him flock impetuously,
Like a great water flood, that tumbling low
From the high mountains, threats to overflow
With sudden fury all the fertile plain,
And the sad husbandman's long hope doth throw
A down the stream, and all his vows make vain,
Nor bounds nor banks his headlong ruin may sustain.

19
Upon his shield their heapéd hail he bore,
And with his sword dispersed the rascal flocks,
Which fled asunder, and him fell before,
As withered leaves drop from their driéd stocks,
When the wroth° western wind does reave° their locks;   *angry / steal*
And underneath him his courageous steed,
The fierce Spumador trode them down[19] like docks,[20]

16. "Conge" is a formal farewell, consisting of a bow/curtsy or sometimes a secret handshake (as you may recall).

17. Arthur sees the castle in peril, arms himself, and rides out to meet the enemies. Particularly, he is in search of their chief who is the "author of that strife." If Arthur can get him, the rest will scatter. As soon as he rides out of the castle, the hoards bend their attentions (and bows) at him.

18. There is probably a double meaning in this line. The main point is to picture the attack of sin like a thick snow storm, a blizzard. But if we consider the image of arrows that "flutter" like flakes of snow, we also realize that there is a sense in which each of the arrows by themselves are not so dangerous; they are weak like a fluttering snowflake. And so too is the attack of sin when viewed through the eyes of faith.

19. I.e., rode over them.

20. A "dock" is another name for a sorrel—a plant of the genus *Rumex,* having leaves that are acid-flavored and which are sometimes, I am told, used in salads. Arthur's horse is a lawnmower.

The fierce Spumador born of heavenly seed:
Such as Laomedon of Phoebus race did breed.[21]

20

Which sudden horror and confuséd cry,
When as their captain heard, in haste he yode°,   *went*
The cause to weet°, and fault to remedy;   *know*
Upon a tiger swift and fierce he rode,
That as the wind ran underneath his load,
Whiles his long legs nigh wrought unto the ground;
Full large he was of limb, and shoulders broad,
But of such subtle substance and unsound,
That like a ghost he seemed, whose grave-clothes were unbound.[22]

21

And in his hand a bended bow was seen,
And many arrows under his right side,
All deadly dangerous, all cruél keen,
Headed with flint, and feathers bloody died,
Such as the Indians[23] in their quivers hide;
Those could he well direct and straight as line,
And bid them strike the mark, which he had eyed,
Nor was there salve, nor was there medicine,
That mote recure° their wounds: so inly° they did tine°.[24]   *heal / inwardly / bite*

22

As pale and wan° as ashes was his look,   *deathly colored*
His body lean and meager as a rake,
And skin all withered like a dried rook,[25]
Thereto as cold and dreary as a snake,
That seemed to tremble evermore, and quake:
All in a canvas thin he was bedight°,   *clothed*
And girded with a belt of twisted brake°,   *brush*

21. Arthur's horse, Spumador, is fierce and noble like those remembered in legends and myths.
22. This is their chief and captain, a deathly looking monster-man with giant limbs, riding a fierce tiger.
23. Not the baseball team.
24. Nothing can cure the injury of these arrows. They are deadly.
25. A bird resembling a crow.

Upon his head he wore an helmet light,
Made of a dead man's skull, that seemed a ghastly sight.[26]

23

Maleger[27] was his name, and after him,
There followed fast at hand two wicked hags,
With hoary° locks all loose, and visage° grim;   grey / appearance
Their feet unshod, their bodies wrapped in rags,
And both as swift on foot, as chaséd stags;
And yet the one her other leg had lame,
Which with a staff, all full of little snags
She did support, and Impotence her name:
But the other was Impatience, armed with raging flame.[28]

24

Soon as the carl° from far the Prince espied,   villain
Glistering in arms and warlike ornament,
His beast he felly° pricked on either side,   furiously
And his mischievous bow full ready bent,
With which at him a cruel shaft he sent:
But he was wary, and it warded° well   blocked
Upon his shield, that it no further went,
But to the ground the idle quarrel fell:
Then he another and another did expel.[29]

25

Which to prevent, the Prince his mortal spear
Soon to him wrought, and fierce at him did ride,
To be avenged of that shot whileare°:   earlier
But he was not so hardy to abide
That bitter stound°, but turning quick aside   moment

26. Their chief is large, but he has no meat. He is pale and ashen, skin and bones. He wears pieces of a human skull for his helmet. Remember how Alma gives strength to her castle-body?

27. Maleger, which comes from the Latin meaning "evil sickness," is intemperance, wasted away and frail. Maleger is an image of the monster that man turns into when infested with sin. There are also allusions to Original Sin, Sin itself, and the Devil. Spenser has created a creature of utmost evil.

28. Maleger is followed by two hags, Impotence and Impatience. Impotence has a lame leg and walks with a staff; Impatience is armed with fire.

29. Maleger shoots many arrows at Prince Arthur. But the Prince defends himself with his shield.

His light-foot beast, fled fast away for fear:
Whom to pursue, the infant[30] after hide,
So fast as his good courser° could him bear,   *horse*
But labor lost it was, to ween° approach him near.   *think to*

26

For as the wingéd wind his tiger fled,
That view of eye could scarce him overtake,
Nor scarce his feet on ground were seen to tread;
Through hills and dales he speedy way did make,
Nor hedge nor ditch his ready passage brake,
And in his flight the villain turned his face,
(As wonts° the Tartar by the Caspian lake,   *does*
When as the Russian him in fight does chase)
Unto his tiger's tail, and shot at him apace°.[31]   *swiftly*

27

Apace he shot, and yet he fled apace,
Still as the greedy[32] knight nigh° to him drew,   *near*
And oftentimes he would relent his pace,
That him his foe more fiercely should pursue:
Who when his uncouth manner he did view,
He 'gan avize° to follow him no more,   *realize*
But keep his standing, and his shafts eschew°,   *fight off*
Until he quite had spent his perilous store,
And then assail him fresh, ere° he could shift° for more.[33] *before / search*

28

But that lame hag, still as abroad he strew°   *spread*
His wicked arrows, gathered them again,
And to him brought, fresh battle to renew:
Which he espying, cast her to restrain
From yielding succor° to that cursed swain,[34]   *aid*

30. Remember the "infant" here is Prince Arthur.

31. Arthur is riding hard after Maleger, but the horse is no match for the tiger in terms of speed. Maleger turns while fleeing and shoots dozens of arrows at Arthur.

32. Arthur is "greedy" in the sense of "hungry" or "ambitious."

33. Arthur realizes that chasing is useless, so he stops pursuing but continues to defend himself from the barrage of arrows. He figures he can wait until Maleger runs out of ammo.

34. A "swain" is a country boy or shepherd boy. It's being used here in an obviously derogatory way, sort of like "hillbilly." Spenser realizes that Impotence is going around fetching Maleger's arrows and returning them to him, so he dismounts and begins tying her up.

And her attacking, thought her hands to tie;
But soon as him dismounted on the plain,
That other hag did far away espy
Binding her sister, she to him ran hastily.

29

And catching hold of him, as down he lent,
Him backward overthrew, and down him stayed
With their rude hands and grisly graplement,[35]
Till that the villain coming to their aid,
Upon him fell, and load upon him laid;
Full little wanted, but he had him slain,
And of the battle baleful° end had made,   *sorrowful*
Had not his gentle Squire beheld his pain,
And coming to his rescue, ere° his bitter bane°.[36]   *before / ruin*

30

So greatest and most glorious thing on ground
May often need the help of weaker hand;
So feeble is man's state, and life unsound,
That in assurance it may never stand,
Till it dissolvéd be from earthly band.
Proof be thou Prince, the prowest° man alive,   *mightiest*
And noblest born of all in Britain land;
Yet thee fierce fortune did so nearly drive,
That had not grace thee blest, thou shouldest not survive.[37]

31

The Squire arriving, fiercely in his arms
Snatched first the one, and then the other jade°,   *disreputable woman*
His chiefest lets° and authors of his harms,   *hindrances*
And them perforce withheld with threatened blade,
Least that his lord they should behind invade;
The whiles the Prince pricked with reproachful shame,
As one awaked out of long slumbering shade,

35. That's the "half nelson" in Spenserian. Impatience sees her little sister getting the "what-for" and comes over and takes Arthur to the ground.

36. After the hag has Arthur down, Maleger is quickly there and on top of him. But Arthur's squire is alert and swift to his aid.

37. I.e., "Even the mightiest men alive can be found weak, since this mortal body is unreliable. Until they are divorced from their earthly ties, sometimes the strongest are given aid by a weaker hand."

Reviving thought of glory and of fame,
United all his powers to purge himself from blame.

32

Like as a fire, the which in hollow cave
Hath long been under kept, and down suppressed,
With murmurous disdain doth inly° rave,   *inwardly*
And grudge, in so straight prison to be pressed,
At last breaks forth with furious unrest,
And strives to mount unto his native seat;
All that did earst° it hinder and molest°,   *formerly / interfere*
It now devours with flames and scorching heat,
And carries into smoke with rage and horror great.[38]

33

So mightily the Briton Prince him roused
Out of his hold, and broke his caitiff° bands,   *cowardly*
And as a bear whom angry curs° have touzed°,   *dogs / upset*
Having off-shaked them, and escaped their hands,
Becomes more fell, and all that him withstands
Treads down and overthrows. Now had the carl°   *villain*
Alighted from his tiger, and his hands
Discharged of his bow and deadly quarrel,
To seize upon his foe flat lying on the marl°.[39]   *ground*

34

Which now him turned to disadvantage dear;
For neither can he fly, nor other harm,
But trust unto his strength and manhood mere°,   *slight*
Since now he is far from his monstrous swarm,
And of his weapons did himself disarm.
The knight yet wrathful for his late disgrace,
Fiercely advanced his valorous right arm,
And him so sore smote with his iron mace,
That groveling to the ground he fell, and filled his place.[40]

38. Arthur is a volcano erupting with righteous anger.
39. Arthur bursts through Maleger's hold, and Maleger is defenseless, having left his bow behind.
40. Having nowhere to turn, Maleger faces Arthur, and Arthur clubs him with his mace, sending him sprawling to the ground.

35

Well weened° he, that field was then his own,   *thought*
And all his labor brought to happy end,
When sudden up the villain overthrown,
Out of his swoon arose, fresh to contend,
And 'gan himself to second battle bend,
As hurt he had not been.[41] Thereby there lay
An huge great stone, which stood upon one end,
And had not been removéd many a day;
Some landmark seemed to be, or sign of sundry way.

36

The same he snatched, and with exceeding sway
Threw at his foe, who was right well aware
To shun the engine of his meant decay;
It booted° not to think that throw to bear,   *helped*
But ground he gave, and lightly leapt arear:
Eft° fierce returning, as a falcon fair   *after which*
That once hath failed of her souse° full near,   *course of attack*
Remounts again into the open air,
And unto better fortune doth herself prepare.[42]

37

So brave returning, with his brandished blade,
He to the carl°[43] himself again addressed,   *villain*
And struck at him so sternly, that he made
An open passage through his riven breast,
That half the steel behind his back did rest;
Which drawing back, he looked evermore
When the heart blood should gush out of his chest,
Or his dead corpse should fall upon the floor;
But his dead corpse upon the floor fell nathemore°.[44]   *none the more*

41. Mace? What mace? It's but a flesh wound!
42. Maleger tosses a huge piece of rock at Arthur, but Arthur dodges out of its way and then returns to face his foe. Maleger may be deathly and frail, but he's still strong.
43. Remember the "carl" is Maleger.
44. Arthur slices all the way through Maleger's chest, but the body doesn't fall any more after it's gored than before. Maleger is what you might call resilient.

38

Nor drop of blood appeared shed to be,
All were the wound so wide and wondrous,
That through his carcass one might plainly see:
Half in amaze° with horror hideous,   *amazement*
And half in rage, to be deluded thus,
Again through both the sides he struck him quite,
That made his sprite° to groan full piteous: *spirit*
Yet nathemore° forth fled his groaning sprite,   *none the more*
But freshly as at first, prepared himself to fight.[45]

39

Thereat he smitten was with great affright,
And trembling terror did his heart appall,
Nor wist° he, what to think of that same sight,   *knew*
Nor what to say, nor what to do at all;
He doubted, lest it were some magical
Illusion, that did beguile his sense,
Or wandering ghost, that wanted funeral,
Or airy spirit under false pretence,
Or hellish fiend raised up through devilish science.[46]

40

His wonder far exceeded reason's reach,
That he began to doubt his dazzled sight,
And oft of error did himself appeach°:   *accuse*
Flesh without blood, a person without sprite°,   *spirit*
Wounds without hurt, a body without might,
That could do harm, yet could not harméd be,
That could not die, yet seemed a mortal wight°,   *creature*
That was most strong in most infirmity;
Like did he never hear, like did he never see.

41

A while he stood in this astonishment,
Yet would he not for all his great dismay
Give over to effect his first intent,
And the utmost means of victory assay°,   *pursue*

45. So you can see through Maleger's body, and yet he continues to take hits. There
is no blood, and he continues to prepare to fight.
46. The "he" is Arthur, who is growing worried that Maleger is unbeatable and is
perhaps some kind of spirit or ghost or demon.

Or the utmost issue of his own decay.
His own good sword Mordure, that never failed
At need, till now, he lightly threw away,
And his bright shield, that naught him now availed,
And with his naked hands him forcibly assailed.[47]

42
Twixt his two mighty arms him up he snatched,
And crushed his carcass so against his breast,
That the disdainful soul he thence dispatched,
And the idle breath all utterly expressed:[48]
Then when he felt him dead, down he cast
The lumpish corse° unto the senseless ground;   *corpse*
Adown he cast it with so puissant° wrest°,   *mighty / grasp*
That back again it did aloft rebound,
And gave against his mother earth a groanful sound.

43
As when Jove's harness-bearing bird from high
Stoops at a flying heron with proud disdain,
The stone-dead quarry falls so forcibly,
That it rebounds against the lowly plain,
A second fall redoubling back again.
Then thought the Prince all peril sure was past,
And that he victor only did remain;
No sooner thought, than that the carl° as fast   *villain*
'Gan heap huge strokes on him, as ere° he down was cast.[49]   *before*

44
Nigh° his wits end then wax° the amazéd knight,   *near / grew*
And thought his labor lost and travail° vain,   *fight*
Against this lifeless shadow so to fight:
Yet life he saw, and felt his mighty mane,
That whiles he marveled still, did still him pain:
Forthy° he 'gan some other ways advise,   *therefore*
How to take life from that dead-living swain°,   *country-boy*

47. After standing dumbfounded for a moment, Arthur throws down his sword and shield and goes after Maleger with his bare hands.

48. I.e., squeezed out. That's what we call in the literary world a "bear hug."

49. This time Maleger is squeezed to death, but when he falls to the ground he rebounds. This would be like throwing a deflated basketball to the ground and having it bounce back up full of air.

Whom still he markéd freshly to arise
From the earth, and from her womb new spirits to reprise°.   *enliven*

45

He then remembered well, that had been said,
How the Earth his mother was, and first him bore;
She eke° so often, as his life decayed,   *also*
Did life with usury to him restore,[50]
And raised him up much stronger than before,
So soon as he unto her womb did fall;
Therefore to ground he would him cast no more,
Nor him commit to grave terrestrial°,   *earthen*
But bear him far from hope of succor° usual.[51]   *relief*

46

Then up he caught him twixt his puissant° hands   *mighty*
And having scruzed° out of his carrion corpse   *squeezed*
The loathful life, now loosed from sinful bands,
Upon his shoulders carried him perforce°   *by necessity*
Above three furlongs, taking his full course,
Until he came unto a standing lake;
Him there into he threw without remorse,
Nor stirred, till hope of life did him forsake;
So end of that carl's° days, and his own pains did make.[52]   *villain's*

47

Which when those wicked hags from far did spy,
Like two mad dogs they ran about the lands,
And the one of them with dreadful yelling cry,
Throwing away her broken chains and bands,
And having quenched her burning fire brands,
Headlong herself did cast into that lake;
But Impotence with her own willful hands,

50. I.e., she gave life to her son at a price. Notice how Mother Earth is on Maleger's side. This pictures the old Adamic man and the old world cursed with the effects of the Fall.

51. Since man came from the earth, it is his mother. Thus Arthur remembers a saying that describes the earth as helping sinful men and providing them with a counterfeit life and nourishment. So Arthur must find a different way to dispatch Maleger.

52. Hooray! Maleger is finally defeated when he is drowned in a lake. This is one of Spenser's pictures of Christian baptism, where by faith the old sinful man is put to death and buried in those waters (Rom. 6:3–4; Col. 2:12).

One of Maleger's cursed darts did take,
So rived° her trembling heart, and wicked end did make.[53]   *pierced*

48

Thus now alone he conqueror remains;
Then coming to his Squire, that kept his steed,
Thought to have mounted, but his feeble veins
Him failed thereto, and served not his need,
Through loss of blood, which from his wounds did bleed,
That he began to faint, and life decay:
But his good Squire him helping up with speed,
With steadfast hand upon his horse did stay,
And led him to the castle by the beaten way.

49

Where many grooms and squires ready were,
To take him from his steed full tenderly,
And eke° the fairest Alma met him there   *also*
With balm and wine and costly spicery,
To comfort him in his infirmity;
Eftsoones° she caused him up to be conveyed,   *soon*
And of his arms despoiled° easily,   *undressed*
In sumptuous bed she made him to be laid,
And all the while his wounds were dressing, by him stayed.[54]

53. The hags, seeing the demise of their master, run around in a cackling frenzy until Impatience drowns herself in the lake and Impotence kills herself with one of Maleger's arrows.

54. After Arthur conquers Maleger and his wicked friends, he is weak from loss of blood, and his squire must aid his return to Alma's castle. There Alma nurses him, dressing his wounds and caring for his needs.

 Off with His Head!

Directions: Identify where in the story the following quotes came from. Explain what they mean and their significance to the story.

1. "Them in twelve troops their captain did dispart
    And round about in fittest steads did place,
    Where each might best offend his proper part,
    And his contrary object most deface."

2. "So greatest and most glorious thing on ground
    May often need the help of weaker hand."

3. "Flesh without blood, a person without sprite,
    Wounds without hurt, a body without might."

Canto XII.

Guyon, by Palmer's governance,
passing through perils great,
Doth overthrow the Bower of bliss,
and Acrasia defeat.

1

Now 'gins this goodly frame of temperance
Fairly to rise, and her adornéd head
To prick of highest praise forth to advance,
Formerly grounded, and fast settled
On firm foundation of true bounty-head°;   *blessing-kindness*
And this brave knight, that for that virtue fights,
Now comes to point of that same perilous stead,
Where pleasure dwells in sensual delights,
'Mongst thousand dangers, and ten thousand magic mights.[1]

2

Two days now in that sea he sailéd has,[2]
Nor ever land beheld, nor living wight°,   *creature*
Nor ought save peril, still as he did pass:
Though when appeared the third morrow bright,

---

1. We have finally reached our intended destination. Guyon must now aim all his powers at defending the virtue of temperance. He is on his way to the Bower of Bliss and will face down the wicked enchantress.

2. You recall that we left Guyon and the Palmer getting into the boat at the beginning of canto 11. They have sailed for two days. It is now the morning of the third day.

Upon the waves to spread her trembling light,
An hideous roaring far away they heard,
That all their senses filled with affright,
And straight they saw the raging surges reared
Up to the skies, that them of drowning made affeard°.   *afraid*

3

Said then the boatman, "Palmer steer aright,
And keep an even course; for yonder way
We needs must pass (God do us well aquite°,)   *acquit*
That is the Gulf of Greediness, they say,
That deep engorgeth° all this world's prey: *swallows*
Which having swallowed up excessively,
He soon in vomit up again doth lay,
And belcheth forth his superfluity°,   *excess*
That all the seas for fear do seem away to fly."[3]

4

On the other side an hideous rock is pight°,   *placed*
Of mighty magnes° stone, whose craggy cliff   *magnet*
Depending from on high, dreadful to sight,
Over the waves his rugged arms doth lift,
And threateneth down to throw his ragged rift
On who so cometh nigh; yet nigh it draws
All passengers, that none from it can shift:
For whiles they fly that gulf's devouring jaws,
They on this rock are rent, and sunk in helpless waves.[4]

5

Forward they pass, and strongly he them rows,
Until they nigh unto that gulf arrive,
Where stream more violent and greedy grows:
Then he with all his puissance° doth strive   *strength*
To strike his oars, and mightily doth drive
The hollow vessel through the threatful wave,

3. This Gulf of Greediness is the first of the dangers Guyon faces on this last part of his journey. The Gulf is a whirlpool of sorts that sucks boats down and then spits them out dead on the rocks. Notice that the Palmer is the one steering the boat. His wisdom and expertise are necessary in navigating the seas.

4. So on the one side is the whirlpool and on the other, jagged cliffs that swirl with foamy tide, pulling ships into their splintering clutches.

Which gaping wide, to swallow them alive,
In the huge abyss of his engulfing grave,
Doth roar at them in vain, and with great terror rave.

6

They passing by, that grisly mouth did see,
Sucking the seas into his entrails° deep,   *stomach*
That seemed more horrible than hell to be,
Or that dark dreadful hole of Tartar steep,[5]
Through which the damned ghosts do often creep
Back to the world, bad livers[6] to torment:
But naught that falls into this direful deep,
Nor that approacheth nigh the wide descent,
May back return, but is condemned to be drowned.

7

On the other side, they saw that perilous rock,
Threatening itself on them to ruinate°,   *ruin*
On whose sharp cliffs the ribs of vessels broke,
And shivered ships, which had been wreckéd late,
Yet stuck, with carcasses exanimate[7]
Of such, as having all their substance spent
In wanton joys, and lusts intemperate,
Did afterwards make shipwreck violent,
Both of their life, and fame for ever foully blent.[8]

8

Forthy°, this hight° The Rock of Vile Reproach,   *therefore / is called*
A dangerous and detestable place,
To which nor fish nor fowl did once approach,
But yelling mews,[9] with seagulls hoarse and base,
And cormorants,[10] with birds of ravenous race,
Which still sat waiting on that wasteful cliff,
For spoil of wretches, whose unhappy case,

5. Spenser compares the Gulf's gulping mouth to the pit of Tartarus, which was believed to be the place of punishment below Hades.

6. Not the organ in your body; this is talking about people who live badly.

7. Use your Latin: *ex* means "out of" or "from" and *animus* means "spirit." So exanimate means "dead" or "without a spirit."

8. That's blown, meaning "wasted."

9. A mew is either another kind of seagull or a bird related to a hawk.

10. This is a term for any sort of large birds that dive into the sea for their prey.

After lost credit and consuméd thrift,
At last them driven hath to this despairful drift.[11]

9

The Palmer seeing them in safety past,
Thus said: "Behold the examples in our sights,
Of lustful luxury and thriftless waste:
What now is left of miserable wights°,   *creatures*
Which spent their looser days in lewd delights,
But shame and sad reproach, here to be read°,   *seen*
By these rent° relics, speaking their ill plights?   *broken*
Let all that live, hereby be counseléd,
To shun Rock of Reproach, and it as death to dread."[12]

10

So forth they rowed, and that ferryman
With his stiff oars did brush the sea so strong,
That the hoar° waters from his frigate° ran,   *white / boat*
And the light bubbles danced all along,
Whiles the salt brine° out of the billows sprung.   *seawater*
At last far off they many islands spy,
On every side floating the floods among:
Then said the knight, "Lo I the land descry,   *discover*
Therefore old sire thy course do thereunto apply."[13]

11

"That may not be," said then the Ferryman
"Lest we unweeting° hap° to be fordone°:   *unknowing / happen / destroyed*
For those same islands, seeming now and then,

11. The Rock and the Gulf are two famous perils from ancient literature. Originally found in Homer's *Odyssey,* they were used again by Virgil in his *Aeneid.* Remember that in Homer, the Skylla was a monster that dwelled in a cave in the side of a cliff. She had twelve feet and six necks and a monstrous head on each neck. Across from her was a sea monster, Charybdis, that was just under the surface of the water, sucking ships and men down into her stomach. In Virgil, these monsters are somewhat receded into the background and "perilous points of rock" and an "abyss" are to the fore. Here in Spenser, there is no mention made of either monster, but these same perils are pictured in more "natural" terms.

12. The Palmer is describing these "natural" phenomena as spiritual or moral disasters to be avoided. The monsters that orchestrate these dangers are sins of lust and waste. Those who live without temperance are ships headed for disaster.

13. The knight is Guyon. He asks to sail towards the islands he sees in the distance.

Are not firm land, nor any certain one,
But straggling plots, which to and fro do run
In the wide waters: therefore are they hight°   *called*
The Wandering Islands. Therefore do them shun;
For they have oft drawn many a wandering wight°   *creature*
Into most deadly danger and distresséd plight.

12

"Yet well they seem to him, that far doth view,
Both fair and fruitful, and the ground dispread
With grassy green of delectable hue,
And the tall trees with leaves appareléd,
Are decked with blossoms dyed in white and red,
That mote° the passengers thereto allure;   *might*
But whosoever once hath fastenéd
His foot thereon, may never it recure°,   *take back*
But wandereth ever more uncertain and unsure.[14]

13

"As the Isle of Delos whilom° men report   *formerly*
Amid the Aegean Sea long time did stray,
Nor made for shipping any certain port,
Till that Latona traveling that way,
Flying from Juno's wrath and hard assay°,   *pursuit*
Of her fair twins was there delivered,
Which afterwards did rule the night and day;
Thenceforth it firmly was established,
And for Apollo's honor highly heried°."[15]   *made known*

14

They to him hearken, as beseemeth meet°,   *right*
And pass on forward: so their way does lie,
That one of those same islands, which do fleet
In the wide sea, they needs must passen by,
Which seemed so sweet and pleasant to the eye,

14. The Wandering Islands are not a wise destination. They appear luscious and green from the distance, but once you set foot onto one, you can never leave. You are cursed to wander for eternity.

15. The Ferryman compares those islands with the Island of Delos, which was much the same as these. It was only finally anchored by supernatural action of the gods. Likewise, wandering men are only anchored and rescued from their wanderings by the unilateral action of the triune God.

That it would tempt a man to touchen there:
Upon the bank they sitting did espy
A dainty damsel, dressing of her hair,
By whom a little skippet° floating did appear.   *boat*

15

She them espying, loud to them can call,
Bidding them nigher draw unto the shore;
For she had cause to busy them withal°;   *with*
And therewith loudly laughed: But nathemore°   *never*
Would they once turn, but kept on as afore:
Which when she saw, she left her locks undight°,   *undone*
And running to her boat withouten ore,
From the departing land it launched light,
And after them did drive with all her power and might.[16]

16

Whom overtaking, she in merry sort
Them 'gan to board, and purpose diversely,
Now feigning dalliance° and wanton sport,   *flirtation*
Now throwing forth lewd° words immodestly;   *obscene*
Till that the Palmer 'gan full bitterly
Her to rebuke, for being loose and light:
Which not abiding, but more scornfully
Scoffing at him, that did her justly wite°,   *rebuke*
She turned her boat about, and from them rowéd quite.

17

That was the wanton Phaedria, which late
Did ferry him over the Idle Lake:[17]
Whom naught regarding, they kept on their gate,
And all her vain allurements did forsake,
When them the wary boatman thus bespake;
"Here now behoveth us well to avise,[18]
And of our safety good heed to take;

    16. As they happen to pass one of the Wandering Islands, they see a woman on the
shore. She calls to them, but being ignored, she takes to her own little boat and begins
sailing towards them.
    17. Having been rebuked by the Palmer, Phaedria realizes her games will go nowhere
with these men, and she hops back in her boat and paddles away.
    18. I.e., "We would do well to consider."

For here before a perilous passage lies,
Where many mermaids haunt, making false melodies.

18
"But by the way, there is a great quicksand,
And a whirlpool of hidden jeopardy,
Therefore, Sir Palmer, keep an even hand;
For twixt them both the narrow way doth lie."[19]
Scarce had he said, when hard at hand they spy
That quicksand nigh with water coveréd;
But by the checked wave they did descry°   *discover*
It plain, and by the sea discoloréd:
It called was the quicksand of Unthriftyhead.[20]

19
They passing by, a goodly ship did see,
Laden from far with precious merchandize,
And bravely furnishéd, as ship might be,
Which through great disadventure, or misprize°,   *mistake*
Herself had run into that hazardous;
Whose mariners and merchants with much toil,
Laboréd in vain, to have recured° their prize,   *recovered*
And the rich wares to save from piteous spoil,
But neither toil nor travail might her back recoil.[21]

20
On the other side they see that perilous pool,
That calléd was the Whirlpool of Decay,
In which full many had with hapless duel
Been sunk, of whom no memory did stay:
Whose circled waters rapped with whirling sway,
Like to a restless wheel, still running round,
Did covet, as they passed by that way,

19. "Narrow is the gate and difficult is the way which leads to life, and there are few who find it" (Mt. 7:14).
20. Unthriftyhead, the lack of shrewd spending habits, is a quicksand that confronts our hero. This is the fifth challenge Guyon has met. Keep track of these perils and consider what they mean.
21. A ship laden with treasure is sinking in the mud of Unthriftyhead. Try as they may, the sailors cannot rescue her from her fate. They will have to give their treasure up or go down with the ship.

To draw their boat within the utmost bound
Of his wide labyrinth, and then to have them drowned.[22]

21

But the heedful boatman[23] strongly forth did stretch
His brawny° arms, and all his body strain,   *muscular*
That the utmost sandy breach they shortly fetch,
Whiles the dread danger does behind remain.
Sudden they see from midst of all the main,
The surging waters like a mountain rise,
And the great sea puffed up with proud disdain,
To swell above the measure of his guise,
As threatening to devour all, that his power despise.

22

The waves come rolling, and the billows roar
Outrageously, as they enraged were,
Or wrathful Neptune did them drive before
His whirling chariot, for exceeding fear:
For not one puff of wind there did appear,
That all the three thereat wax° much afraid,   *grew*
Unweeting°, what such horror strange did rear.   *not knowing*
Eftsoones° they saw an hideous host arrayed,   *presently*
Of huge sea monsters, such as living sense dismayed.[24]

23

Most ugly shapes, and horrible aspects,
Such as Dame Nature self mote° fear to see,   *might*
Or shame, that ever should so foul defects
From her most cunning hand escapéd be;

22. Notice how they keep coming to dangers that are on either side of them, forcing them to keep a straight course: first the Rock and the Gulf, now the Quicksand and the Whirlpool. This teaches us an important lesson that whenever we face a trial or temptation it's a good bet that there is an equally dangerous counter-danger on the other side. One example of this is how alcoholism has tempted many people to avoid alcohol altogether even to the point of disobeying our Lord's command to drink wine at the Lord's Supper. Both are dangerous and threaten the well-being of any ship in those waters. We, like the Palmer, must steer a straight course and, like the boatman, paddle hard. Temperance is the ability to see the ditch on either side of the road and keep to the middle. Obedience avoids whatever danger we face.

23. The Boatman and the Ferryman are the same burly man.

24. Without a breeze in the air, a giant tidal wave emerges from the depths of the sea carrying with it a host of monstrous sea creatures.

All dreadful portraits of deformity:[25]
Spring-headed hydras,[26] and sea-shouldering whales,
Great whirlpools, which all fishes make to flee,
Bright scolopendras,[27] armed with silver scales,
Mighty Monoceroses,[28] with immeasuréd tails.

24

The dreadful fish, that hath deserved the name
Of death, and like him looks in dreadful hue,
The grisly wasserman,[29] that makes his game
The flying ships with swiftness to pursue,
The horrible sea-satyr,[30] that doth show
His fearful face in time of greatest storm,
Huge ziffius°, whom mariners eschew°   *swordfish / avoid*
No less, than rocks, as travelers inform,
And greedy rosmarines° with visages° deform.   *walruses / appearances*

25

All these, and thousand thousands many more,
And more deforméd monsters thousand fold,
With dreadful noise, and hollow rumbling roar,
Came rushing in the foamy waves enrolled,
Which seemed to fly for fear, them to behold:
Nor wonder, if these did the knight appall;
For all that here on earth we dreadful hold,
Be but as bugs to fearing babes withal,
Compared to the creatures in the seas enthrall.[31]

25. Notice that all these monsters are "deformities." Intemperance is always a deformity and therefore an "ugly shape and horrible aspect." True temperance is whole and lovely.

26. Hydras are water serpents with many heads. The most famous was slain by Hercules.

27. These are giant ocean centipedes.

28. These are seahorses with a single horn. Think unicorn with fins and tail.

29. This is a merman—a man from the waist up, a fish from the waist down.

30. A satyr is a wicked goat-man from ancient mythology, known for lascivious living. Satyrs are even mentioned in the Bible! Funny thing, some moderns have begun translating the Hebrew word for "satyr" as orangutan or baboon.

31. Spenser says that compared with sea monsters, the beasts we face on land are mere bugs.

Unicorns

Could there really have been any such thing as a unicorn? Well the short answer is yes. History is replete with tales and legends of swift horses (often flying) with a single, noble horn upon their face. The Authorized Version of the Bible (or King James Version) also mentions unicorns in a number of places in the Old Testament (e.g., Job 39:9–12; Ps. 92:10). Unfortunately for those of us with modern translations, the word for unicorn is usually translated as "wild ox." Modern scholars as a whole are incredibly unimaginative and frankly quite scared of anything that may point to the general verity of fairy tales. These unicorns are often waved away with explanations that if you look at a double horned ox from the side, it looks like it only has one horn, as if the ancients were thick-headed and foolish.

While the Hebrew word for unicorn doesn't necessarily mean that a unicorn only had one horn, the biblical idea of a horse-like creature having only one horn seems to have been solidified by the Septuagint which was the Greek translation of the Old Testament prior to the coming of Christ. It is fairly humorous that it is often a tooth and a knee cap within a couple of yards of one another that provide archeologists with evidence necessary to sketch several billion years of human development. It seems rather plain that scientists tend to find whatever it is they're looking for no matter how ridiculous. With this sort of goofiness passing for intelligent scholarship, modern evaluations of ancient mythology are hardly to be trusted. It also stands to reason that our unicorn may be hiding among the many dynasties of dinosaurs now recorded. Perhaps he's crouched down politely in the corner amongst pterodactyls, waiting patiently for us to remember him. Ancient man may not have had personal computers or automobiles, but they are no less our forefathers and deserving of our honor. They have left us many stories about this ancient creature, and it would dishonor their record to so easily discredit them. In a world of elephants and tigers and puffins, unicorns seem almost rather too normal to belong but certainly not too strange.

26

"Fear not," then said the Palmer well avized°;   *studied*
"For these same monsters are not these indeed,
But are into these fearful shapes disguised
By that same wicked witch, to work us dread,
And draw from on this journey to proceed."
Then lifting up his virtuous staff on high,
He smote the sea, which calméd was with speed,[32]
And all that dreadful army fast 'gan fly
Into great Tethys' bosom,[33] where they hidden lie.[34]

27

Quit from that danger, forth their course they kept,
And as they went, they heard a rueful cry
Of one, that wailed and pitifully wept,
That through the sea the resounding plaints° did fly: *complaints*
At last they in an island did espy
A seemly maiden, sitting by the shore,
That with great sorrow and sad agony,
Seemed some great misfortune to deplore,
And loud to them for succor° calléd evermore.   *help*

28

Which Guyon hearing, straight his Palmer bade°,   *asked*
To steer the boat towards that doleful° maid,   *sad*
That he might know, and ease her sorrow sad:
Who him avising° better, to him said;   *knowing*
"Fair sir, be not displeased, if disobeyed:
For ill it were to hearken to her cry;
For she is inly° nothing ill apaid,[35]   *inwardly*
But only womanish fine forgery,
Your stubborn heart to affect with frail infirmity.

29

"To which when she your courage hath inclined
Through foolish pity, then her guileful bait

32. Hmmm . . . sounds familiar. Hasn't someone done something like this before?
33. Tethys was a Titan sea-goddess.
34. The Palmer says that all those monsters are under a spell of the witch Acrasia. He lifts his staff and strikes the water; they disperse leaving the waters calm.
35. I.e., "There's nothing really wrong with her."

She will embosom° deeper in your mind,   *bury*
And for your ruin at the last await."[36]
The knight was ruled, and the boatman strait
Held on his course with stayéd steadfastness,
Nor ever shrunk, nor ever sought to bait°   *rest*
His tired arms for toilsome weariness,
But with his oars did sweep the watery wilderness.[37]

30

And now they nigh approached to the stead,
Where as those mermaids dwelt: it was a still
And calmy bay, on the one side sheltered
With the broad shadow of an hoary° hill,   *white*
On the other side an high rock towered still,
That twixt them both a pleasant port they made,
And did like an half theatre fulfill:
There those five sisters had continual trade,
And used to bathe themselves in that deceitful shade.

31

They were fair ladies, till they fondly strived
With the Heliconian maids for mastery;
Of whom they overcome, were deprived
Of their proud beauty, and the one moiety°   *half*
Transformed to fish, for their bold surquedry°,   *overconfidence*
But the upper half their hue retained still,
And their sweet skill in wonted° melody;   *accustomed*
Which ever after they abused to ill,
To allure weak travelers, whom gotten they did kill.[38]

36. A maiden stranded on a beach crying for help . . . This is another ploy. Guyon
wants to steer towards her and help, but the Palmer warns Guyon of the danger. She is
like Phaedria, but where Phaedria attempted to lure Guyon with giggles and fun, this
maiden tries to lure with pity, trying to make Guyon feel sorry for her.

37. Even here at the end of Guyon's journey he is still in need of advice and correc-
tion from wise companions. A mark of a temperate man is one who surrounds himself
with faithful friends who aren't afraid to withstand him if he starts to head in the wrong
direction. "Faithful are the wounds of a friend. But the kisses of an enemy are deceitful"
(Prov. 27:6).

38. Next, they sail by five mermaids who had once been beautiful ladies, but after
challenging a few Muses to a contest were punished by having their lower half turned
into a fin. All that they have left of their beauty is their voices with which they seek to
lure travelers. They are quite a bit like the Sirens from Homer's *Odyssey* that lured sailors
with their enchanted melodies.

32

So now to Guyon, as he passed by,
Their pleasant tunes they sweetly thus applied;
"O thou fair son of gentle faerie,
That art in mighty arms most magnified
Above all knights, that ever battle tried,
O turn thy rudder hither-ward a while:
Here may thy storm-beat vessel safely ride;
This is the port of rest from troublous toil,
The world's sweet inn, from pain and wearisome turmoil."[39]

33

With that the rolling sea resounding soft,
In his big bass them fitly answered,
And on the rock the waves breaking aloft,
A solemn mean unto them measured,
The whiles sweet Zephyrus[40] loud whistled
His treble, a strange kind of harmony;
Which Guyon's senses softly tickled,
That he the boatman bade row easily,
And let him hear some part of their rare melody.[41]

34

But him the Palmer from that vanity°,   *view*
With temperate advice discounseled°,[42]   *discouraged*
That they it past, and shortly 'gan descry°   *discover*
The land, to which their course they leveled;
When suddenly a gross fog over spread
With his dull vapor all that desert has,
And heaven's cheerful face enveloped,
That all things one, and one as nothing was,
And this great universe seemed one confuséd mass.

39. Beautiful, psycho mermaids singing songs and offering rest—who could resist?
40. That's the Greek god of the western wind.
41. The mermaids have a false harmony and beauty that is quite alluring. Guyon asks the Boatman to slow down just a touch so he can listen.
42. Guyon doesn't want to actually go to the mermaids; he just wants to slow down and listen for a bit. He doesn't agree with the whole murder bit, but their music could make for a good party. But even slowing to listen is giving in.

35

Thereat they greatly were dismayed, nor wist°   *knew*
How to direct their way in darkness wide,
But feared to wander in that wasteful mist,
For tumbling into mischief unespyed°.   *unseen*
Worse is the danger hidden, than descride°.   *seen*
Suddenly an innumerable flight
Of harmful fowls about them fluttering, cried,
And with their wicked wings them oft did smite,
And sore annoyed, groping in that grisly night.[43]

36

Even all the nation of unfortunate
And fatal birds about them flockéd were,
Such as by nature men abhor and hate,
The ill-faced owl, death's dreadful messenger,
The hoarse night-raven, trump of doleful drear,
The leather-wingéd bat, day's enemy,
The rueful strich°, still waiting on the bier,[44]   *screech owl*
The whistler shrill, that who so hears, doth die,
The hellish harpies, prophets of sad destiny.

37

All those, and all that else does horror breed,
About them flew, and filled their sails with fear:
Yet stayed they not, but forward did proceed,
Whiles the one did row, and the other stiffly steer;
Till that at last the weather 'gan to clear,
And the fair land itself did plainly show.
Said then the Palmer, "Lo where does appear
The sacred soil, where all our perils grow;
Therefore, sir knight, your ready arms about you throw."[45]

38

He hearkened, and his arms about him took,
The whiles the nimble boat so well her sped,

43. This is Spenser's tribute to Hitchcock's classic *The Birds*. Just as they spy their destination in the distance, a great fog sweeps over them. Too worried about hitting something in the dark, they slow down, and after a minute they are inundated with birds.

44. A "bier" is a coffin (what we put dead bodies in before we bury them) and its stand. All these birds are in some way symbolically related to death.

45. They sail on through the fog and birds, and when they spot the land once again, the Palmer tells Guyon to arm himself and be ready when they reach the shore.

That with her crooked keel the land she struck,
Then forth the noble Guyon sallied°,   *leapt*
And his sage Palmer, that him governéd;
But the other by his boat behind did stay.
They marchéd fairly forth, of naught ydread,[46]
Both firmly armed for every hard assay°,   *attack*
With constancy and care, 'gainst danger and dismay.

39

Ere° long they heard an hideous bellowing   *before*
Of many beasts, that roaréd outrageously,
As if that hunger's point, or Venus' sting
Had them enraged with fell surquedry°;   *arrogance*
Yet naught they feared, but past on heartily,
Until they came in view of those wild beasts:
Who all at once, gaping full greedily,
And rearing fiercely their upstarting crests,
Ran towards, to devour those unexpected guests.[47]

40

But soon as they approached with deadly threat,
The Palmer over them his staff upheld,
His mighty staff, that could all charms defeat:
Eftsoones° their stubborn courages were quelled°,   *immediately / shrunk*
And high advancéd crests down meekly felled,
Instead of fraying°, they themselves did fear,   *fighting*
And trembled, as them passing they beheld:
Such wondrous power did in that staff appear,
All monsters to subdue to him, that did it bear.[48]

46. I.e., they marched with no fear.
47. They are not traveling long when they come upon a pack of wild beasts who, seeing them, rush towards the newcomers.
48. The Palmer's staff reduces the fierce beasts to cowering animals. These beasts were once men. They have been seduced and transformed by Acrasia's magic. This is an honest picture of the power of lust and immorality to make men into beasts. The real world is still full of this kind of magic. Also of note is the fact that this is the last trial for Guyon to face before he arrives at the Bower of Bliss. From the beginning of this canto until now, Guyon has faced twelve tests. Notice also that these tests end on stanza 40. Remember that during Noah's flood, it rained for forty days and nights, Israel spent forty years in the wilderness, and Jesus was tested by the devil for forty days in the desert. Forty is the number of trial and testing. Guyon has passed; he is now ready for the showdown.

41

Of that same wood it framed was cunningly,
Of which Caduceus whilom° was made,   *formerly*
Caduceus the rod of Mercury,
With which he wonts° the Stygian° realms invade,   *usually / Hellish*
Through ghastly horror, and eternal shade;
The infernal fiends with it he can assuage°,   *calm*
And Orcus[49] tame, whom nothing can persuade,
And rule the Furies, when they most do rage:
Such virtue in his staff had eke° this Palmer sage.[50]   *also*

42

Thence passing forth, they shortly do arrive,
Whereas the Bower of Bliss was situate;
A place picked out by choice of best alive,
That nature's work by art can imitate:
In which whatever in this worldly state
Is sweet, and pleasing unto living sense,
Or that may daintiest fantasy aggrate°,   *imagine*
Was pouréd forth with plentiful dispense,
And made there to abound with lavish affluence°.[51]   *luxury*

43

Goodly it was enclosed round about,
As well their entered guests to keep within,
As those unruly beasts to hold without;
Yet was the fence thereof but weak and thin;
Naught feared their force, that fortilage° to win,   *fortress*
But wisdom's power, and temperance's might,
By which the mightiest things efforcéd° been: *overpowered*
And eke° the gate was wrought of substance light,   *also*
Rather for pleasure, than for battery or fight.[52]

49. Orcus is another name for Pluto, the god of Hades.
50. The Palmer's staff is made from the same wood as Mercury's rod, Caduceus, and is able to tame even hellish fiends.
51. At last we have come to the Bower of Bliss. It is a castle with grounds that try to imitate the beauties of nature and is filled with every lavish richness.
52. The Bower of Bliss is guarded by a flimsy gate, though that's usually all that was needed. They fear nothing save the might and strength of wisdom and temperance. Each of these qualities are personified in the Palmer and Sir Guyon.

44

It framéd was of precious ivory,
That seemed a work of admirable wit;
And therein all the famous history
Of Jason and Medea was ywrit°;   *written*
Her mighty charms, her furious loving fit,
His goodly conquest of the golden fleece,
His falséd faith, and love too lightly flit,
The wondered Argo, which in venturous peace
First through the Euxine seas bore all the flower of Greece.

45

Ye might have seen the frothy billows fry
Under the ship, as thorough° them she went,   *through*
That seemed the waves were into ivory,
Or ivory into the waves were sent;
And other where the snowy substance spread
With vermeil°, like the boy's blood therein shed,   *red*
A piteous spectacle did represent,
And other-whiles with gold besprinkled;
It seemed the enchanted flame, which did Creüsa wed.[53]

46

All this, and more might in that goodly gate
Be read; that ever open stood to all,[54]
Which thither came: but in the porch there sat
A comely personage of stature tall,
And semblance° pleasing, more than natural,   *appearance*
That travelers to him seemed to entice;
His looser garment to the ground did fall,
And flew about his heels in wanton wise,
Not fit for speedy pace, or manly exercise.[55]

53. Jason, according to this story, sailed in the Argo to find the Golden Fleece. With Medea's magical powers they retrieved it and then ran away together, throwing pieces of her brother's body into the sea in order to evade capture. After Jason ditched Medea, she sent his new bride, Creusa, a piece of clothing that burned her to death when she put it on. This tale shows both the lust of a man (Jason) and the seducing and destructive powers of a wicked woman (Medea).

54. Every way of life has a story at its center. Every culture or religion has a gospel, a heroic tale that gives meaning and direction to life. Here, even Acrasia the Enchantress has a story woven into the walls of her bower. The story is of seduction and treachery.

55. This fellow's clothing is so baggy he would have had a hard time keeping up in a foot race.

47

They in that place him Genius did call:
Not that celestial power, to whom the care
Of life, and generation of all
That lives, pertains in charge particular,
Who wondrous things concerning our welfare,
And strange phantoms doth let us oft foresee,
And oft of secret ill bids us beware:
That is our self, whom though we do not see,
Yet each doth in himself it well perceive to be.

48

Therefore a god him sage Antiquity
Did wisely make, and good Agdistes call:[56]
But this same was to that quite contrary,
The foe of life, that good envies to all,
That secretly doth us procure to fall,
Through guileful semblance°, which he makes us see.   *appearance*
He of this garden had the governal°,   *rule*
And pleasure's porter was devised to be,
Holding a staff in hand for more formality.[57]

49

With diverse flowers he daintily was decked,[58]
And strewed round about, and by his side
A mighty mazer° bowl of wine was set,   *wooden*
As if it had to him been sacrificed;
Wherewith all new-come guests he gratified:
So did he eke° Sir Guyon passing by: *also*
But he his idle courtesy defied,
And overthrew his bowl disdainfully;
And broke his staff, with which he charméd semblance° sly.[59]   *appearance*

56. Spenser says that this man's name is Genius, but he clarifies here that he is not referring to the natural smarts and wisdom that are endowed to man being made in the image of God.

57. This is a counterfeit "Genius." Even lust and wickedness put up a false front of reason and coherence.

58. This guy's what we call a "girly-man."

59. Temperance knows when to ignore the blather of idiots and crash their empty party. Here, Guyon kicks over the bowl of wine and breaks Genius' staff. He too has a staff, but it is not used like the Palmer's. He is a false wisdom.

50

Thus being entered, they behold around
A large and spacious plain, on every side
Strewed with pleasance, whose fair grassy ground
Mantled with green, and goodly beautified
With all the ornaments of Flora's pride,
Wherewith her mother Art, as half in scorn
Of niggard° Nature, like a pompous bride   *greedy*
Did deck her, and too lavishly adorn,
When forth from virgin bower she comes in the early morn.[60]

51

Thereto the heavens always jovial,
Looked on them lovely, still in steadfast state,
Nor suffered storm nor frost on them to fall,
Their tender buds or leaves to violate,
Nor scorching heat, nor cold intemperate
To afflict the creatures, which therein did dwell,
But the mild air with season moderate
Gently atempered, and disposed so well,
That still it breathed forth sweet spirit and wholesome smell.[61]

52

More sweet and wholesome, than the pleasant hill
Of Rhodope, on which the nymph, that bore
A giant babe, herself for grief did kill;
Or the Thessalian Tempe, where of yore
Fair Daphne Phoebus heart with love did gore;
Or Ida, where the gods loved to repair°,   *vacation*
When ever they their heavenly bowers forlore°;   *left*
Or sweet Parnasse, the haunt of muses fair;
Or Eden self, if ought° with Eden mote° compare.[62]   *anything / might*

60. Like a loose woman, this land is recognized by being overdressed and overpainted. It's ostentatious: shiny and plastic.

61. This is the evil of sentimentalism and the unfortunate nature of what passes for "Christian art." The world often depicted is some imaginary temperate paradise, as though God had not created a world with the beauties of snow or blood or dirt.

62. False pleasures always have some true and good pleasure twisted and distorted. Even this land has aspects that would appear to have true beauty at first. This is what makes lust and other false pleasure so dangerous: it gives an impression of beauty on the surface. It always puts its best foot forward, so to speak.

53

Much wondered Guyon at the fair aspect
Of that sweet place, yet suffered no delight
To sink into his sense, nor mind affect,
But passéd forth, and looked still forward right,
Bridling his will, and mastering his might:[63]
Till that he came unto another gate,
No gate, but like one, being goodly dight°   *covered*
With boughs and branches, which did broad dilate°   *expand*
Their clasping arms, in wanton wreathings intricate.

54

So fashioned a porch with rare device,
Arched overhead with an embracing vine,
Whose bunches hanging down, seemed to entice
All passersby, to taste their luscious wine,
And did themselves into their hands incline,
As freely offering to be gathered:
Some deep empurpled as the hyacinth,
Some as the ruby, laughing sweetly red,
Some like fair emeralds, not yet well ripened.

55

And them amongst, some were of burnished gold,
So made by art, to beautify the rest,
Which did themselves amongst the leaves enfold,
As lurking from the view of covetous guest,
That the weak boughs, with so rich load oppressed,
Did bow adown, as over-burdenéd.
Under that porch a comely dame did rest,
Clad in fair weeds°, but foul disorderéd,   *clothes*
And garments loose, that seemed unmeet for womanhood.[64]

56

In her left hand a cup of gold she held,
And with her right the riper fruit did reach,
Whose sappy liquor, that with fullness swelled,
Into her cup she squeezed, with dainty breach

63. This is a lesson that young men need to master in particular: sometimes it is necessary to look straight ahead and walk, bridling our will and mastering our might.
64. They come up to a porch that is covered in vines with juicy grapes—purple, red, and golden. Sitting under the vines, loosely dressed, is a young and beautiful woman.

Of her fine fingers, without foul impeach,
That so fair wine-press made the wine more sweet:
Thereof she used to give to drink to each,
Whom passing by she happened to meet:
It was her guise°, all strangers goodly so to greet.   *deception*

57

So she to Guyon offered it to taste;
Who taking it out of her tender hand,
The cup to ground did violently cast,
That all in pieces it was broken found,
And with the liquor stained all the land:
Whereat Excess exceedingly was wroth°,   *angry*
Yet no'te° the same amend, nor yet withstand,[65]   *could not*
But suffered him to pass, all were she loath;
Who naught regarding her displeasure forward goeth.[66]

58

There the most dainty paradise on ground,
Itself doth offer to his sober eye,
In which all pleasures plenteously abound,
And none does other's happiness envy:
The painted flowers, the trees up shooting high,
The dales for shade, the hills for breathing space,
The trembling groves, the crystal running by;
And that, which all fair works doth most agrace,
The art, which all that wrought, appearéd in no place.

59

One would have thought, (so cunningly, the rude,
And scornéd parts were mingled with the fine,)
That nature had for wantonness ensued
Art, and that Art at nature did repine;
So striving each the other to undermine,
Each did the other's work more beautify;
So differing both in wills, agreed in fine:

65. I.e., she couldn't do anything to fix it, and she couldn't stand up against Guyon.
66. The woman's name is Excess. She, like Genius, holds a cup of wine to offer those who come by, but Guyon, wanting nothing to do with her wine, takes the cup and flings it to the ground. Excess is quite mad, but she cannot do anything in response, and the Palmer and Guyon continue past her.

So all agreed through sweet diversity,
This garden to adorn with all variety.[67]

60

And in the midst of all, a fountain stood,
Of richest substance, that on earth might be,
So pure and shiny, that the silver flood
Through every channel running one might see;
Most goodly it with curious imagery
Was over-wrought, and shapes of naked boys,
Of which some seemed with lively jollity,
To fly about, playing their wanton toys,
Whilst others did themselves embay° in liquid joys.　　　　　　　　　*swim*

61

And over all, of purest gold was spread,
A trail of ivy in his native hue:
For the rich metal was so colored,
That wight°, who did not well avised° it view,　　　*informed / creature*
Would surely deem it to be ivy true:[68]
Low his lascivious° arms adown did creep,　　　　　　　　　*immoral*
That themselves dipping in the silver dew,
Their fleecy flowers they tenderly did steep,
Which drops of crystal seemed for wantons to weep.

62

Infinite streams continually did well
Out of this fountain, sweet and fair to see,
The which into an ample laver fell,
And shortly grew to so great quantity,
That like a little lake it seemed to be;
Whose depth exceeded not three cubit's height,
That through the waves one might the bottom see,
All paved beneath with jasper shining bright,
That seemed the fountain in that sea did sail upright.

67. Here, in the heart of the Bower of Bliss, the garden puts forth its most lovely effects. Spenser says the beauty is so overwhelming that the ugliness (which is present) fades into the background and is nearly impossible to see. Art and Nature seem to be in perfect harmony.

68. I.e., if you didn't know better you'd think the ivy was real. This and other hints are Spenser's clues showing us how the beauty of the Bower of Bliss is fake.

63

And all the margent° round about was set,   *margin*
With shady laurel trees, thence to defend
The sunny beams, which on the billows beat,
And those which therein bathed, mote° offend.   *might*
As Guyon happened by the same to wend°,   *go*
Two naked damsels he therein espied,
Which therein bathing, seemed to contend,
And wrestle wantonly, nor cared to hide,
Their dainty parts from view of any, which them eyed.[69]

64

Sometimes the one would lift the other quite
Above the waters, and then down again
Her plunge, as over mastered by might,
Where both awhile would covered remain,
And each the other from to rise restrain;
The whiles their snowy limbs, as through a veil,
So through the crystal waves appearéd plain:
Then suddenly both would themselves unheal°,   *uncover*
And the amorous[70] sweet spoils to greedy eyes reveal.

65

As that fair star, the messenger of morn,
His dewy face out of the sea doth rear:
Or as the Cyprian goddess, newly born
Of the ocean's fruitful froth, did first appear:
Such seeméd they, and so their yellow hair
Crystalline humor° dropped down apace.   *moisture*
Whom such when Guyon saw, he drew him near,
And somewhat 'gan relent his earnest pace,
His stubborn breast 'gan secret pleasance to embrace.[71]

66

The wanton maidens him espying, stood
Gazing a while at his unwonted° guise°;   *unacccustomed / habit*

69. As Guyon is walking by the fountain, he notices two women who are bathing beneath the shade of the trees. They don't seem to mind him seeing them naked.

70. You know, like *amor.*

71. As Guyon looks at the women, he begins to slow his steps, and he begins to desire what is not rightfully his. Thousands of excuses could be running through his mind—"Well you know, it's sort of artistic . . ." or, "It's only natural . . ."

Then the one herself low ducked in the flood,
Abashed, that her a stranger did avise°:   *see*
But the other rather higher did arise,
And her two lily paps° aloft displayed,   *breasts*
And all, that might his melting heart entice
To her delights, she unto him bewrayed°:   *called*
The rest hid underneath, him more desirous made.[72]

67

With that, the other likewise up arose,
And her fair locks, which formerly were bound
Up in one knot, she low adown did loose:
Which flowing long and thick, her clothéd around,
And the ivory in golden mantle gowned:
So that fair spectacle from him was reft°,   *taken*
Yet that, which reft it, no less fair was found:
So hid in locks and waves from lookers theft,
Naught but her lovely face she for his looking left.[73]

68

Withall she laughed, and she blushed withall,
That blushing to her laughter gave more grace,
And laughter to her blushing, as did fall:
Now when they spied the knight to slack his pace,
Them to behold, and in his sparkling face
The secret signs of kindled lust appear,
Their wanton merriments they did increase,
And to him beckoned, to approach more near,
And showed him many sights, that courage cold could rear.[74]

72. Seeing that Guyon is watching them, one of the women ducks beneath the water and the other exposes herself more fully and calls to Guyon to join her.

73. The first woman comes back out of the water, letting her hair down as a sorry excuse for clothes.

74. Guyon has come perhaps to the toughest battle yet. Intemperance begs him to stay and watch and see what will happen. He is being attacked with the open and direct assault of the woman who "bares all," as well as the no less dangerous assault of the slightly embarrassed woman who is showing nothing but her "lovely face." Spenser points out that these sights and pleasures are enjoyed by "courage cold." It takes no courage at all to succumb to the temptations of lust. It's as easy as being a coward. This is also a lesson in modesty. Fully covered or fully bare: the heart is still revealed in word and action.

69

On which when gazing him the Palmer saw,
He much rebuked those wandering eyes of his,
And counseled well, him forward thence did draw.[75]
Now are they come nigh to the Bower of Bliss
Of her fond favorites so named amiss°:   *wrongly*
When thus the Palmer: "Now sir, well avize°;   *understand*
For here the end of all our travel is:
Here wons° Acrasia, whom we must surprise,   *lives*
Else she will slip away, and all our drift despise."[76]

70

Etfsoones° they heard a most melodious sound,   *presently*
Of all that mote° delight a dainty ear,   *might*
Such as at once might not on living ground,
Save in this paradise, be heard elsewhere:
Right hard it was, for wight°, which did it hear,   *creature*
To read, what manner music that mote° be: *might*
For all that pleasing is to living ear,
Was there consorted in one harmony,
Birds, voices, instruments, winds, waters, all agree.

71

The joyous birds shrouded in cheerful shade,
Their notes unto the voice atempered sweet;
The angelical soft trembling voices made
To the instruments divine respondence meet°:   *fitting*
The silver sounding instruments did meet
With the bass murmur of the water's fall:
The water's fall with difference discreet,
Now soft, now loud, unto the wind did call:
The gentle warbling wind low answeréd to all.[77]

72

There, whence that music seemed heard to be,
Was the fair witch herself now solacing,

75. Guyon makes a number of mistakes here, but the Palmer reprimands him first for his "wandering eyes."

76. The Palmer tells Guyon that they have finally come to Acrasia herself, but they must use stealth, otherwise she will escape. The element of surprise is a weapon against the immoral.

77. All the sounds of nature combine to create a lovely harmony.

With a new lover, whom through sorcery
And witchcraft, she from far did thither bring:
There she had him now laid a slumbering,
In secret shade, after long wanton joys:
Whilst round about them pleasantly did sing
Many fair ladies, and lascivious° boys,   *immoral*
That ever mixed their song with light licentious° toys°.[78]   *wicked / games*

73

And all that while, right over him she hung,
With her false eyes fast fixed in his sight,
As seeking medicine, whence she was stung,
Or greedily depasturing° delight: *devouring*
And oft inclining down with kisses light,
For fear of waking him, his lips bedewed°,   *moist*
And through his humid eyes did suck his sprite°,   *life*
Quite molten° into lust and pleasure lewd;   *melted*
Wherewith she sighéd soft, as if his case she rued°.   *pitied*

74

The whiles someone did chant this lovely lay°:   *song*
"Ah see, who so fair thing doest feign to see,
In springing flower the image of thy day;
Ah see the virgin rose, how sweetly she
Doth first peep forth with bashful modesty,
That fairer seems, the less ye see her may;
Lo see soon after, how more bold and free
Her baréd bosom she doth broad display;
Lo see soon after, how she fades, and falls away.

75

"So passeth, in the passing of a day,
Of mortal life the leaf, the bud, the flower,
Nor more doth flourish after first decay,
That earst° was sought to deck both bed and bower,   *before*
Of many a lady, and many a paramour°:   *lover*
Gather therefore the rose, whilest yet is prime,
For soon comes age, that will her pride deflower:

---

78. There is a whole choir of women and boys playing and singing, and in the midst
of them is Acrasia, finishing off her latest victim, a young man, bewitched by her spells
and sorcery and far from home.

Gather the rose of love, whilest yet is time,
Whilest loving thou may'st loved be with equal crime."[79]

76

He ceased, and then 'gan all the choir of birds
Their diverse notes to tune unto his lay,
As in approvance° of his pleasing words.   *approval*
The constant pair heard all, that he did say,
Yet swervéd not, but kept their forward way,
Through many covert groves, and thickets close,
In which they creeping did at last display
That wanton lady, with her lover loose,
Whose sleepy head she in her lap did soft dispose.[80]

77

Upon a bed of roses she was laid,
As faint through heat, or dight° to pleasant sin,   *given*
And was arrayed, or rather disarrayed,[81]
All in a veil of silk and silver thin,
That hid no wit her alabaster skin,
But rather showed more white, if more might be:
More subtle web Arachne cannot spin,
Nor the fine nets, which oft we woven see
Of scorchéd dew, do not in the air more lightly flee.[82]

78

Her snowy breast was bare to ready spoil
Of hungry eyes, which n'ote° therewith be filled,   *could not*

79. The point of the song is essentially to praise young love. The rose, the song tells us, is more beautiful at the first, which is of course a metaphor for a woman. But like all lies, there is only a degree of truth here. Proverbs does command each man to rejoice in the wife of his youth (Prov. 5:18) and to behold and enjoy her. Yet the Proverb goes on to say that she should satisfy "at all times" (5:19). The lie of the song is that young love is better than old love, so go for it now. But while there is immense blessing in every stage of love, the truth is that love is like wine and it improves with time. We know this to be true ultimately because God has loved the Church, and we do not fear that He will grow tired of us, or that our love will grow old and wither.

80. The "constant pair" is the Palmer and Guyon. They press through thickets and groves, stealing swiftly and silently nearer to the witch and her victim.

81. I.e., she was clothed, or rather unclothed.

82. Her fair skin, Spenser says, was far more subtle a web than even the finest Arachne could spin.

And yet through languor° of her late sweet toil,   *exhaustion*
Few drops, more clear than nectar, forth distilled,
That like pure orient pearls adown it trailed,
And her fair eyes sweet smiling in delight,
Moistened their fiery beams, with which she thrilled
Frail hearts, yet quenchéd not; like starry light
Which sparkling on the silent waves, does seem more bright.[83]

79

The young man sleeping by her, seeméd to be
Some goodly swain° of honorable place,   *lad*
That certes° it great pity was to see   *surely*
Him his nobility so foul deface;
A sweet regard, and amiable grace,
Mixed with manly sternness did appear
Yet sleeping, in his well proportioned face,
And on his tender lips the downy hair
Did now but freshly spring, and silken blossoms bear.[84]

80

His warlike arms, the idle instruments
Of sleeping praise, were hung upon a tree,
And his brave shield, full of old monuments,
Was foully 'rased°, that none the signs might see;   *erased*
Nor for them, nor for honor cared he,
Nor ought, that did to his advancement tend,
But in lewd loves, and wasteful luxury,
His days, his goods, his body he did spend:
O horrible enchantment, that him so did blind.

81

The noble elf°, and careful Palmer drew   *Guyon*
So nigh them, minding naught, but lustful game,
That sudden forth they on them rushed, and threw
A subtle net, which only for the same
The skillful Palmer formally did frame.[85]

83. Notice that Acrasia's breast is laid bear for "hungry eyes" but cannot fill, and her eyes smile, thrilling weak hearts, but "quenched not." Her body promises to be food and drink, but it does not satisfy hunger or thirst. It's like eating air.

84. He's a young man because he's just starting to show facial hair.

85. As Acrasia spun a net to capture hapless men, so she is caught in a net—surely a proverbial justice.

So held them under fast, the whiles the rest
Fled all away for fear of fouler shame.
The fair enchantress, so unwares oppressed,
Tried all her arts, and all her sleights, thence out to wrest°.   *undo*

82

And eke° her lover strove: but all in vain;   *also*
For that same net so cunningly was wound,
That neither guile, nor force might it distrain°.   *break*
They took them both, and both them strongly bound
In captive bands, which there they ready found:
But her in chains of adamant° he tied;   *strength*
For nothing else might keep her safe and sound;
But Verdant (so he hight°) he soon untied,   *was named*
And counsel sage instead thereof to him applied.[86]

83

But all those pleasant bowers and palace brave,
Guyon broke down, with rigor pitiless;
Nor ought their goodly workmanship might save
Them from the tempest of his wrathfulness,
But that their bliss he turned to balefulness°:   *shame*
Their groves he felled, their gardens did deface,
Their arbors° spoil, their cabinets° suppress,   *trees / cottages*
Their banquet houses burn, their buildings raze,
And of the fairest late, now made the foulest place.[87]

84

Then led they her away, and eke° that knight   *also*
They with them led, both sorrowful and sad:
The way they came, the same returned they right,

86. Acrasia needs strong ropes, whereas her victim needs a bit of detox and wise counsel. This episode parallels the story of Mordant (canto 2). The name Mordant means "death-giving" whereas Verdant means "green-giving" or "life-giving." Mordant was taken down by Acrasia; he tasted the fruit of her lips which was death and death to his family (Amavia and Ruddymane, symbolically). But Verdant was saved by Guyon and the Palmer. He was given life, and now he is called to give life to others.

87. Temperance demands total destruction of the Bower of Bliss and all such wickedness. There is no room for dialogue or sorting through the pieces. Such pity would be intemperate and cowardly. Temperance binds the whore and topples her kingdom. Spenser knows this and shows this, a biting critique of many modern Christians who in general have the courage and effect of the common house fly: a bit of a nuisance but easily done away with.

Till they arrivéd, where they lately had
Charméd those wild-beasts, that raged with fury mad.
Which now awaking, fierce at them 'gan fly,
As in their mistress's rescue, whom they led;
But them the Palmer soon did pacify.
Then Guyon asked, "What meant those beasts, which there did lie?"

85
Said he, "These seeming beasts are men indeed,
Whom this Enchantress hath transforméd thus,
Whilom° her lovers, which her lusts did feed,   *formerly*
Now turnéd into figures hideous,
According to their minds like monstrous."
"Sad end," quoth he, "of life intemperate,
And mournful mead° of joys delicious: *reward*
But Palmer, if it mote° thee so aggrate°,   *might / please*
Let them returnéd be unto their former state."[88]

86
Straight way he with his virtuous staff them struck,
And straight of beasts they comely men became;
Yet being men they did unmanly look,
And staréd ghastly, some for inward shame,
And some for wrath, to see their captive dame:
But one above the rest in speciál,
That had an hog been late, hight° Grill by name,   *called*
Repinéd greatly, and did him miscall°,   *denounce*
That had from hoggish form him brought to natural.[89]

87
Said Guyon, "See the mind of beastly man,
That hath so soon forgot the excellence
Of his creation, when he life began,
That now he chooseth, with vile differénce,
To be a beast, and lack intelligence."

88. Guyon asks the Palmer what the deal is with those beasts that keep charging after them. The Palmer explains that the beasts were once men who have been changed by Acrasia's spells. They are the refuse pile of Acrasia, they're the men she's done with. Then Guyon asks the Palmer to turn them back into men.

89. Some of the men are embarrassed and realize right away what had happened. Others are mad that Acrasia is bound up, and one in particular, Grill, is quite angry about being turned back into a man. He would rather remain a pig than be a man. What a fool.

To whom the Palmer thus, "The dunghill kind
Delights in filth and foul incontinence:
Let Grill be Grill, and have his hoggish mind,
But let us hence depart, whiles weather serves and wind."[90]

90. The wicked witch is overthrown and her Bower of Bliss is nothing but rubble. Temperance doesn't mean being mild; it means full-on zealous pursuit of godliness and holiness and a complete hatred for the wickedness of sin. Though the "strange woman" may be beautiful and her bed decked with rich ornaments, she is a deep pit. To seek her is to seek death, and all those who go after her are scorned by God. May God have mercy on us and give us all the strength and courage to tear down the strongholds of evil and fearlessly face down the Acrasias of our day.

Let Grill Be Grill

Directions: Identify where in the story the following quotes came from. Explain what they mean and their significance to the story.

    1. "Ere long they heard an hideous bellowing
       Of many beasts, that roaréd outrageously,
       As if that hunger's point, or Venus' sting
       Had them enraged with fell surquedry."

    2. "One would have thought, (so cunningly, the rude,
       And scornéd parts were mingled with the fine,)
       That nature had for wantonness ensued
       Art, and that Art at nature did repine."

    3. "His warlike arms, the idle instruments
       Of sleeping praise, were hung upon a tree."

Appendix

Spenser's *Faerie Queene, Book II*
The Legend of Sir Guyon, Knight of Temperance: A Play

retold by Toby J. Sumpter

CAST OF CHARACTERS

Archimago	Belphoebe	Diet
Guyon	Phedon	Appetite
Duessa	Occasion	Concoction
Palmer	Furor	Digestion
Redcross	Atin	Maleger
Amavia	Pyrochles	Impotence
Sir Huddibras	Cymochles	Impatience
Sansloy	Phaedria	Squire
Medina	Mammon	Boatman
Elissa	Prince Arthur	Genius
Perissa	Servant	Excess
Braggadochio	Alma	Acrasia
Trompart	Porter	

SCENE 1

SCENE: An open space in a forest area.

(ARCHIMAGO *is sneaking around.*)

ARCHIMAGO: I'm the cunning architect of cankered guile. I was recently bound in chains, but now I'm free to roam and seduce the world with my schemes. Particularly, I hate that Redcross Knight and all his friends! May his sword be flimsy like spaghetti! Uh-oh . . . here they come!

(ARCHIMAGO *hides, seeing* GUYON *and the* PALMER *coming.*)

GUYON: And then I swung my mighty sword down upon his wicked neck and severed through and—

PALMER: (*Slightly amused/annoyed*) Guy-on! If I hear that tale one more time I think I might—

GUYON: (*Whispering*) Man in the bushes.

PALMER: No I wouldn't hide in the bushes! I'd—

GUYON: (*Whispering louder*) Man in the bushes.

PALMER: What?

GUYON: (*Clenching his teeth and taking* PALMER'S *head and turning it with his hand to* ARCHIMAGO) Man . . . in . . . the bushes.

PALMER: Yes, yes, man in the bushes . . . Man in the—?

GUYON: Excuse me! Hello there! Man in the bushes!

ARCHIMAGO: (*Coming out of the bushes, slightly embarrassed*) Uh . . . yes, ummm . . . I mean . . . (*In stately voice*) Fair Son of Mars! I greet thee and thy warlike company! Please won't you stop for such a humble old man like me?

GUYON: (*To the company*) Whoa! (*Now turning and responding to* AR-CHIMAGO) Fine sir, please tell us of your problems.

ARCHIMAGO: (*Pretending to be scared*) I just saw, not far back, a young maiden lying on the path, clothes ripped and hair disheveled. I believe some villain has acted most dishonorably toward her.

GUYON: (*Bursting with anger*) Where is this vile and treasonous knight? Why when I get my hands on that pile of good for nothing . . . (*Pauses*) No, no . . . I take that back . . . when I get my sword on that . . . (*His words trail off as he rides away in haste*)

(*Stage clears.* GUYON *rides in to find* DUESSA *sitting on the ground crying.*)

GUYON: Fair maiden! For what reason do you cry?

DUESSA: (*Hiding her face*) I cry because my honor has been torn away by some wicked man!

GUYON: Who is this vile miscreant? Where did he go? What did he look like?

DUESSA: I don't know his name, but he rode a gray horse, and he had a silver shield marked with a bloody cross.

GUYON: (*Gasps in disbelief*) I don't believe my ears! I remember that knight. He was such a good man! (*Angry again*) Well, shortly he'll be paying for this wicked deed!

DUESSA: Oh . . . Thank you! You're my hero!

(ARCHIMAGO *enters, sidling up to* GUYON.)

ARCHIMAGO: I've seen the wretched man that did this! Come! This way!

(ARCHIMAGO *leads* GUYON *up a hill and points down at* REDCROSS.)

ARCHIMAGO: There's your man! (*Aside*) Or little girl more likely . . .

(*Without a word,* GUYON *lifts his sword and charges* REDCROSS. RED-CROSS *begins to arm himself, and at the last minute* GUYON *stops.*)

GUYON: Uh . . . hi . . . sorry about that. (*Fakes a laugh*) I just realized that you're not the Dark Overlord of All Malice and Ill.

REDCROSS: (*Confused*) Yeah, you're right, Guyon. What in the name of Shirley Temple were you doing?

GUYON: Well, you see . . . ummm . . . well it's a long story.

REDCROSS: Try me.

GUYON: Well . . . an old man? . . . a dishonored young lady? . . . a little too much spur in the head?

REDCROSS: Okay, nevermind. Next time just be more careful.

GUYON: Okay . . . sorry again. I'll be seeing you around?

REDCROSS: Yes, but hopefully you won't greet me with the same enthusiasm every time.

GUYON: It's a deal.

(*They shake hands.* GUYON *sees his* PALMER *in the distance, waves to* REDCROSS, *and leaves.*)

SCENE 2

(GUYON *and* PALMER *travel on. Nearby is a forest.*)

AMAVIA: (*From the woods, screaming*) AAAAAHHHHHHHH! If heaven hates me so, then I wish for death! Come then! Come soon! Come sweet Death to me! AAAAAHHHHH! . . . (*She stabs herself and moans*) Oooohhh . . .

(GUYON *and the* PALMER *come rushing up and find Sir Mordant dead in the grass,* AMAVIA *stabbed* (*Still breathing*), *and her small child lying in her blood.*)

GUYON: Who are you? Why are you doing this?

(*There's no response from* AMAVIA.)

PALMER: What is your deal?!

AMAVIA: (*Gasping for breath*) God hates me!

GUYON: Now come on! It can't be that bad.

AMAVIA: My husband Mordant was seduced by the wicked Acrasia! He fell under her spells of lust and now he's dead because she cast a spell on his cup and (*Screaming again*) now I want to die! (*She slumps over acting dead*)

GUYON: Excuse me, excuse me. (*Shaking her body*) Would you mind telling me why you don't mind leaving this baby here in the middle of the woods all alone? Is it your baby?

AMAVIA: (*Reviving momentarily*) Oh yeah . . . I almost forgot . . . take this child . . . care for him as your own . . . thanks . . . and now I must die . . . (*She slumps over, acting dead again*)

GUYON: (*Shaking her again*) And you say this lady's name is Acrasia?

AMAVIA: (*Reviving again, horrified*) YES! STAY AWAY FROM HER CASTLE! It's called (*In dark tone*) the Bower of Bliss . . . and now I must die . . . (*She slumps over dead*)

GUYON: (*To the* PALMER) Well, I guess that's that. Not much else to be done but wash this baby off in this little stream here. (*Starts washing him*) Huh . . . that's funny . . . it won't come off . . . useless water!

PALMER: (*Shaking his head*) Don't you know anything? That's because there was this nymph. She was running away from some kissy-face satyr. She called for help, and Diana, she's the goddess of chastity, saved her by turning her into a statue. Now her tears run forever down into this creek. She was so pure that this water cannot be tainted by anything, especially the bloody hands of a child.

GUYON: Oh.

(GUYON *and* PALMER, *with the baby march until they happen to come by Medina's Castle. As they approach* SIR HUDDIBRAS *and* SANSLOY *are in the middle of a sword fight.*)

SIR HUDDIBRAS: And take that you ninny!

SANSLOY: Ha! You missed, you sissy faced coward!

SIR HUDDIBRAS: At least I'm not afraid of the dark!

SANSLOY: Hey! You promised not to tell!

SIR HUDDIBRAS: Well, I crossed my fingers! Ha! Gotcha! (*He swings and gets* SANSLOY *in the arm*)

SANSLOY: (*Screaming*) Aaaaahhhhhhhh! You big snail eater!

(GUYON *sees the fight and charges into the middle of it. They keep fighting and calling each other names like "lizard brain," "elf head," and "dandelion breath." Finally* MEDINA *rushes up to them.*)

MEDINA: By the mothers that bore you! By the ladies you love! By the oaths that you swore! I demand that you stop!

ELISSA and PERISSA: Booo! Booo! Fight! Fight! Fight!

MEDINA: (*At the top of her lungs*) Huddibras! Sansloy!

(*They both stop fighting immediately and snap to attention.*)

SIR HUDDIBRAS and SANSLOY: (*Together*) Yes ma'am.

MEDINA: Come inside, it's time to eat now.

(*They all go in and sit at a table set with food.*)

SIR HUDDIBRAS: (*Excitedly*) Oooohhh! Foooood!

(*They all sit down to eat, and right away the sisters start quarrelling.*)

PERISSA: (*In a loud voice*) Hey! Elissa, why don't you eat something? It's goooood stuff!

ELISSA: I do not need any food. It would make me sick.

PERISSA: Oh come on! At least laugh a little, enjoy the meal a little . . . have some wine!

ELISSA: I can't image anything more disgusting . . . how much of that stuff have you had?

PERISSA: (*Giggling, though somewhat proudly*) Two bottles after this glass!

MEDINA: So tell us, sir knight, who you are and what sort of gallant mission a knight such as yourself is on.

GUYON: I serve the beautiful Glorianna and with the Palmer's help, I'm sworn to go and destroy the works of that false Acrasia, whose false deeds are too wicked to be told.

MEDINA: Tell on!

GUYON: Well, you see . . . first . . .

(GUYON *begins telling, but it's getting late and soon everyone falls asleep.*)

SCENE 3

(BRAGGADOCHIO and TROMPART *are walking along a road and meet* ARCHIMAGO.)

ARCHIMAGO: (*Squinting*) Who goes there?!

TROMPART: It is only us, Trompart and Braggadochio, brave knights of courage and valor!

ARCHIMAGO: Oh yeah? Well I've got a job for you. You see there's this knight going around acting like he's hot stuff, but really he's wicked. His name is Sir Guyon, but he's a murderer and a vile man.

BRAGGADOCHIO: (*Angry*) Don't worry, old man! We'll find that nasty bugger and teach 'im a thing or two!

TROMPART: Yeah, yeah! You tell 'im, Braggy!

BRAGGADOCHIO: Don't call me Braggy.

TROMPART: That's right! You'll teach 'im a thing or two, old Braggy.

BRAGGADOCHIO: Don't call me Braggy.

TROMPART: You said it! Old—

(BRAGGADOCHIO *grabs* TROMPART *by the neck and gives him "the look."*)

ARCHIMAGO: All you need is a sword!

BRAGGADOCHIO: Nope, I don't need one. I can take 'im with me bare hands!

ARCHIMAGO: Look, there's this Prince Arthur guy. He's got a magic sword—I'll get it for you. (ARCHIMAGO vanishes.)

BRAGGADOCHIO and TROMPART: (*Look at each other, then run away screaming*) AAAHHHHHH! (*They stop running when they come to some woods. Suddenly, they spot someone in the woods, sprinting towards them.*)

BRAGGADOCHIO: (*Running to hide in some nearby bushes*) Help, help!

(BELPHOEBE *enters, running.*)

BELPHOEBE: Hullo! Did you seen a deer come through here recently with an arrow in its side?

TROMPART: (*Shaking with fear*) Uh . . . no ma'am . . . no deer . . . uh . . . uh . . . nope.

BELPHOEBE: Huh. Well he's got to be around here somewhere.

BRAGGADOCHIO: (*Seeing who it is, comes out of the bushes, trying to act brave*) Hey-hey, what a beautiful little lass you are! What are you doing out here in the wild?

BELPHOEBE: I am a hunter.

BRAGGADOCHIO: Your home should be in a court or palace with other beautiful people!

BELPHOEBE: The court makes people lazy and then they get into trouble. I pursue honor and thus I must work hard and stay busy. I think that—

BRAGGADOCHIO: (*Rushing toward her to steal a kiss*) Come here my dainty piece of chocolate, my sweet little charming—

BELPHOEBE: (*Smacks him in the face and brandishes her sword*) You're a punk!

(BRAGGADOCHIO *cowers in fear for a moment, then* BELPHOEBE *disappears back into the wood.*)

TROMPART: (*Nervously*) Well, that wasn't so bad . . . I mean . . . I guess it could have been worse.

BRAGGADOCHIO: (*Proudly*) Yeah! I would have kissed her more if I hadn't thought she was a goddess. Funny thing, I'm not afraid of anything, except gods and goddesses. When I heard her coming I figured it was one them, so that's why I hid. But I'm not afraid.

TROMPART: (*Looking at him questioningly*) Hmmm . . .

(BRAGGADOCHIO *and* TROMPART *exit, continuing their journey.* GUYON *and* PALMER *enter.*)

GUYON: (*Pointing at someone in the distance*) Who's that?

PALMER: I don't know, but I think we're about to find out.

(PHEDON *enters, being beaten by* OCCASION *and* FURY. GUYON *rushes forward and grabs* OCCASION *and* FURY *and ties them up.*)

GUYON: (*Turning to* PHEDON) What happened to you?!

PHEDON: Oh thank you so much . . . I don't know . . . I don't know . . . it's such a long story. My life is such a mess! I was engaged and then my best friend tricked me and I killed my fiancée's servant and my best friend, and I've been hunting for my fiancée ever since to kill her too!

GUYON: Wow. That's a mess.

PHEDON: Yeah.

(ATIN *comes rushing in on horseback.*)

GUYON: Hello there! Who are you and what do you seek?

ATIN: I am Atin, servant of Pyrochles, great knight in the land! I come seeking Occasion for my master, who looks for a fight!

GUYON: (*Laughing*) You're looking for *who?*

ATIN: Occasion! You know—short old hag, pretty ugly?

GUYON: Yeah, I know the one you're talking about, I just don't know why you'd want her. I just tied her up over there (*Pointing*). So you'll just have to go back and tell your master that there's no chance she's being freed. He'll have to go cry to his mommy.

ATIN: (*Enraged*) WHAT? You'll be sorry you ever said such a thing! My master will, will, will . . . will do something bad to you! (*He rides away in anger.*)

SCENE 4

(GUYON *and* PALMER *are waving goodbye to* PHEDON, *who exits.*)

GUYON: Poor fella, I sure hope things turn out for him.

PALMER: Yeah, he wasted most of his life being beaten by Fury.

(*Suddenly* PYROCHLES *rides up and swings his sword at* GUYON. GUYON *puts his shield up just in time. The sword bounces off the shield and cuts off the head of Pyrochles' horse.* PYROCHLES *falls to the ground.*)

PYROCHLES: What have you done?! I'm gonna slash your brains to the moon! (PYROCHLES *begins swinging wildly at* GUYON. GUYON *blocks carefully and has* PYROCHLES *running into various items on stage. Finally* GUYON *hits* PYROCHLES *in the head and knocks him down.* ATIN *sees his master beaten and runs for help.*)

PYROCHLES: Please kill me quickly. Don't let me suffer!

GUYON: I'm not gonna kill you . . . I just want to know what your problem is.

PYROCHLES: (*Whining*) Well . . . I just want you to let Occasion and Fury go . . .

GUYON: Is that all! Well, if that's all you want, I don't think it's a good idea, but have it your way. (GUYON *sets* OCCASION *and* FURY *free. They start beating* PYROCHLES *right away.*)

PYROCHLES: Help! Help!

PALMER: Don't help him, he asked for it. As soon as you tie them up again, he'll be demanding their release.

SCENE 5

(CYMOCHLES, *accompanied by* ATIN, *is coming to get revenge for his brother's defeat.*)

ATIN: (*Finishing his story for* CYMOCHLES) And then he said that he could go cry to his mommy!

CYMOCHLES: WHAT? He said that? Oh . . . I'm gonna mess that guy's face up.

(*They come to a body of water, which is Idle Lake.*)

CYMOCHLES: Now let's see here . . . How do we get across this? . . . Hmmm . . .

PHAEDRIA: (*In a cutesy voice*) Yoohoo! Over here! (*Blows kisses*) Right this way! I'll give you a ride across the lake!

(CYMOCHLES *gets on board and we watch as she sweet talks him to the other side. He falls asleep, and she lays him down on the ground. About this time we see* GUYON *and the* PALMER *approaching the same river.* PHAEDRIA *moves in for another "kill."*)

PHAEDRIA: (*Again in cutesy voice*) Yoohoo! Over here! (*Blows kisses*) Right this way! I'll give you a ride across the lake!

(GUYON *goes across with* PHAEDRIA. *When they arrive,* CYMOCHLES *is just waking up, and seeing* GUYON, CYMOCHLES *charges at him.*)

CYMOCHLES: You nasty, nasty man! I heard what you have done to my brother, Pyrochles! For this dishonor, you will pay! You are a sissy-man, and you deserve to chew on my sword!

GUYON: (*Getting upset*) Oh really? (GUYON *and* CYMOCHLES *begin sword fighting.*)

CYMOCHLES: (*Swinging his sword wildly*) Take that! And that! And that! You're so weak; little children could beat you up!

GUYON: You talk big, but can your sword back you up? (GUYON *strikes* CYMOCHLES *once, and* CYMOCHLES *strikes* GUYON *once.*)

PHAEDRIA: Please! Please! Stop this madness! Why do you strike at each other seeking death? Can't we all just get along? (*Sweetly*) There is another battle that I prefer, it is sweet and soft and full of Cupid's song and poetry!

(GUYON *and* CYMOCHLES *stop fighting.*)

GUYON: Fine! I'll stop, but you have to get me out of here now!

PHAEDRIA (*Still trying to seduce him*) As you wish . . . (*They get in her boat, and as they reach the other side of Idle Lake, they see* ATIN *and* PYROCHLES *running around madly.*)

ATIN: (*Screaming in fear*) Aaaaahhhh!

PYROCHLES: (*Screaming in pain*) Aaaaahhhh!

GUYON: What's the deal? Hey! What's wrong?

ATIN: (*Crying*) There's something wrong with my master!

PYROCHLES: (*Sloshing around in the lake*) I burn! I burn! I burn! Ouch! Ouch! Eww! Ahhh! Ouch! Ouch! Hot! Hot! Hot!

ARCHIMAGO: You look closer to drowning, than burning to death. But I'll find you some help.

SCENE 6

(*After arriving on the other side of the lake,* GUYON *sees* MAMMON *and* MAMMON *tries to quickly hide his riches.*)

GUYON: Hey! Hey! Who are you?

MAMMON: Uh . . . nothing!

GUYON: What's a guy as ugly as you doing with all that gold?

MAMMON: I'm not ugly.

GUYON: Umm . . . yeah, it looks like your neck threw up.

MAMMON: (*Angry*) WHAT? . . . Well . . . all this gold is mine! You hear? All mine! I am the great ruler of the earth! I give riches and life and I take it away! Hahahaha! Hahahaha!

GUYON: Huh. So basically you scare everybody by rubbing your face with battery acid? And then you make them give you all their money?

MAMMON: No! Don't you know that money makes the world go round? And I have all of the money of the world in my power! If you will swear allegiance to me and kiss my feet, I will make you a great man in the earth!

GUYON: Kiss your feet? I'd rather poke my own eyes out.

MAMMON: Fine! Have it your way, but before you make your final decision, why don't I show you around a little. Right this way.

(*They enter a nearby cave and come into a large, dark room.*)

MAMMON: Ta-da! This is it! Isn't this great?

GUYON: Uh . . . well . . . what do you call it?

MAMMON: Why don't you know? This is the deep darkness below, the underworld, the last stop before eternal damnation! You've come a long way, Guyon. Now welcome to Hell!

GUYON: Hmmm . . . I figured as much.

MAMMON: Let me introduce you to some of my friends. (*Pointing them out as he goes*) That's Revenge. Careful—he bites. There's Spite and Treason, and over there are Hate and Jealousy. Over in the corner, yeah, that's Fear. Watch out—he spits. Down this way. (*He continues leading* GUYON *down the hallway.*) Ahh, yes! This is Sorrow and his bunk-buddy, Shame. And if you squint up into that corner you can just make out the eyes of a truly despicable character. His name is Horror. Isn't this place wonderful? Can't you just smell the foulness? Can't you just taste the repulsiveness? Don't you just want to make yourself at home?

GUYON: You know Mammon, I am really impressed.

MAMMON: (*Excited*) I know . . .

GUYON: I am just amazed . . . some of your friends are uglier than you!

(MAMMON *growls.* GUYON *and* MAMMON *step into a new room.*)

MAMMON: Here, before us, is the goal of all men. Before us is the bliss of all the earth!

GUYON: Even better than swords?

MAMMON: Yes!

GUYON: I don't believe it.

MAMMON: Ta-da! It's my daughter, Philotime! The most beautiful woman ever to walk the streets of earth! (*There are a bunch of people gathered around her; she motions to* GUYON.) If you will bow to me, I will give her to you as your wife, to have and to hold from this day forth and—

GUYON: Gee, thanks, Mister Ugly Face, but I don't want any of this business! I serve the true King and I am already betrothed unto another who is far prettier than any money-god's harlot! Let me go! I will not serve you or your band of fools!

MAMMON: Fine! Let's get out of here.

(*As they are leaving the underworld,* GUYON *has grown weary and he faints as they leave the shadows. In the distance,* PYROCHLES *and* CY-MOCHLES *are sneaking up. The* PALMER *enters and sees them.*)

PYROCHLES: Haha! Now we've got 'im!

CYMOCHLES: Yes! We'll make Swiss cheese out of his insides!

PALMER: You get away, you heathen pansies! Don't you have any honor? You can't attack a man who's fallen in weariness.

PYROCHLES: Oh can't we? I don't see why not.

CYMOCHLES: Yeah, I don't see any rule books lying around, do you? And anyways, it's probably a sign from heaven. He deserves to die!

PALMER: You'll have to fight me first if you want to get at the good Sir Guyon.

(*Suddenly* PRINCE ARTHUR *rides in on a horse.*)

PRINCE ARTHUR: Hello there! What seems to be the trouble?

PALMER: These two pagan ninnies are trying to fillet a good man while he sleeps!

PRINCE ARTHUR: Stand back or I'll mow you down with my trusty spear.

CYMOCHLES: You think we're afraid of you, all by yourself?

PYROCHLES: (*Sarcastically*) Oh no! I think we should call our mommy! Hahaha!

PRINCE ARTHUR: Then prepare to meet your doom. (PRINCE ARTHUR *begins swinging at the two, and the fight begins. It's back and forth for a while, and* PRINCE ARTHUR *is even wounded a couple of times. During the fight, the* PALMER *offers Guyon's sword to* PRINCE ARTHUR. *With it, he kills* CYMOCHLES.)

PRINCE ARTHUR: There! (*Turning to* PYROCHLES) Now do you want to die too? I will give you life if you will just surrender and swear to quit your evil deeds!

PYROCHLES: (*Sadly*) Okay.

PRINCE ARTHUR: REALLY?

PYROCHLES: (*Bitterly*) NO! What do you take me for? I'd rather die than give you anything! AAAHHHHHH! (PYROCHLES *charges at* PRINCE ARTHUR. PRINCE ARTHUR *cuts his head off.*)

PRINCE ARTHUR: (*Shaking his head and walking away*) I've never understood these types. Always smelled a little funny too.

SCENE 7

(PRINCE ARTHUR and GUYON *are walking and come to the House of Alma. There's a band of wild creatures surrounding it and trying to attack it.*)

GUYON: Well, what do we have here? Looks like a party for ugly creatures. I bet you and I won't be able to get in . . . we're not ugly enough.

PRINCE ARTHUR: Yeah . . . They probably make you promise to poke holes in your face to be part of their club!

GUYON: I think we should go break up the party. Maybe we can rest in the castle for a while. I'm beat.

PRINCE ARTHUR: Last one to the castle is a rotten turnip! (PRINCE ARTHUR *and* GUYON *charge into the group and make a swift defeat of the foul creatures.*)

PRINCE ARTHUR: (*Knocking on the door of the House of Alma*) Hello! Hello there! I don't suppose these folks will be bothering you anymore!

SERVANT: Well I'll be! Sweet molasses! We ain't had no peace in these parts for at least seven years! And you two be the first knights that ever beat them ghouls and goblins down! Great Jehosaphat! Come on in!

(PRINCE ARTHUR *and* GUYON *enter and are met by* ALMA.)

ALMA: (*Curtsying*) Good day, fair sirs. We are indebted to your service. Thank you so kindly. Come this way, we will care for all of your needs. But first let me give you a short tour. This is the Porter.

PORTER: How do you do?

PRINCE ARTHUR: Well, thank you.

GUYON: Uh . . . little sore . . . haven't had any grub in a while.

ALMA: This is the cook by the name of Diet and his good friend Appetite.

DIET and APPETITE: Hello!

PRINCE ARTHUR and GUYON: Hi.

ALMA: And down this hall is where the fire always burns, mixing and burning and churning. Ah yes! And there's the cook, Concoction, and his sidekick, the honorable Digestion.

CONCOCTION: Hey-hey! Wanna peanut?

PRINCE ARTHUR and GUYON: (*Looking at each other*) No thanks.

DIGESTION: Watch your step there. We had a poor guy slip down those steps a couple of weeks ago. He ended with his head stuck in the mashed potatoes.

GUYON: Thanks. We'll watch out for the spuds.

ALMA: And in through this room . . .

(*The tour continues until finally they come to the library.*)

ALMA: And here's the library, and the—

GUYON and PRINCE ARTHUR: BOOKS! (*They run into the library and begin picking out books to read.*)

PRINCE ARTHUR: Oh yeah! I found one called *Briton Monuments!*

GUYON: That's nothing! I found *The Antiquity of Faerie Land!*

PRINCE ARTHUR: (*To* ALMA) May we please read these books?

GUYON: Oh please! Please! Please! Please!

ALMA: Why of course . . . enjoy! (ALMA *exits, leaving them to their books.*)

SCENE 8

(PRINCE ARTHUR *is waving good-bye to* GUYON *and the* PALMER, *who are journeying to the Bower of Bliss. After they leave,* MALEGER *enters, approaching the House of Alma.*)

MALEGER: (*Riding on a tiger and shooting several arrows at* PRINCE ARTHUR) Braahahhaghghg phrgshaghghaghagh! (*Rides off*)

(PRINCE ARTHUR *begins running after him but sees* IMPOTENCE *and* IMPATIENCE *gathering up all of the arrows and preparing to give them back to* MALEGER.)

PRINCE ARTHUR: (*Running up to them*) Hey! You've done just about enough here.

(IMPOTENCE *and* IMPATIENCE *turn on* PRINCE ARTHUR *and attack him. They're just about to kill him, when the* SQUIRE *arrives.*)

SQUIRE: Whoa there, ladies! There seems to be some mistake! You've got my master! (*He pulls them off* PRINCE ARTHUR *and ties them up. Just as* PRINCE ARTHUR *is rescued,* MALEGER *sneaks up behind him.* PRINCE ARTHUR *sees* MALEGER *and charges at him.*)

PRINCE ARTHUR: So we meet at last! Whoa! (*Stops suddenly*) I wish Guyon could see you! I bet you're as ugly as Mammon! What do you have all those feathers for? You look like a rotten turkey!

MALEGER: (*Rushing at* PRINCE ARTHUR) Braahaghgh-mraghhfraghgh-hghghgh!

PRINCE ARTHUR: Excuse me but I don't think you've brushed your teeth in a while . . . PHEW!

MALEGER: Braaahahahahghghg!

PRINCE ARTHUR: Well sorry. I just don't understand your speech. (PRINCE ARTHUR *swings and puts his sword through* MALEGER'S *chest.* MALEGER *just stands there.*)

MALEGER: (*Charging at* PRINCE ARTHUR *again*) Braahahahahghghgh-ghghg!

(PRINCE ARTHUR *looks in amazement at* MALEGER *and then his sword and in the end throws his sword down and charges at* MALEGER *bare-handed.*)

PRINCE ARTHUR: Well, if trusty Mordure won't help me, I'll give you a super-duper rib crusher! (PRINCE ARTHUR *gives* MALEGER *the biggest bear hug he can.* MALEGER *falls down, and* PRINCE ARTHUR *brushes his hands together and begins walking away.*)

MALEGER: (*Getting up and rushing at* PRINCE ARTHUR) Brraahahaha-hahghghghghgh!

PRINCE ARTHUR: All right! That's it! (PRINCE ARTHUR *grabs* MALEGER *and carries him to a nearby lake and tosses him in.*) In you go! See ya later, shark bait!

(IMPATIENCE *dives in after* MALEGER *and drowns with him, and* IMPO-TENCE *finds a dart and stabs herself.*)

SCENE 9

(GUYON, PALMER, *and* BOATMAN *are sailing to the Bower of Bliss.*)

GUYON: Swab the decks, ye mateys! Man the poop! Rig the riggings!

PALMER: (*Rolling his eyes*) Guyon! This is a sailboat—there is no poop deck.

GUYON: Oh right . . . ummm . . . well . . . STEADY AS SHE GOES!

PALMER: (*Shaking his head*) Aye-aye, Captain.

GUYON: Halt! Who's that over there? Some poor girl is stranded on the beach . . . shouldn't we go help her?

PALMER: NO! It's a trap! Many men have gotten this far seeking to destroy the Bower of Bliss and they have been drawn into her web of slimy power! Keep us moving, Boatman!

BOATMAN: Aye-aye, Captain! Watch your rearview mirrors though! We've got some company coming!

GUYON: Aaaahhhhhhh! It's a huge army of sea monsters! AAAaahhhh! There's seahorses and whales and mermen and satyrs and walruses and swordfish and five-headed serpents! Aaahhh!

BOATMAN: AAAaaaahhhhhhhhh! We're all gonna die!

PALMER: HOLD IT! (*Silence*) It's a magic that plagues these poor creatures, but there is deeper magic still! (*He strikes the sea with his rod and the sea is calm and the monsters return to the waves.*)

BOATMAN and GUYON: PHEW! That was a close one. (*They continue sailing for a while till they reach the shore. As they come on to the land a number of beasts come rushing toward them.*)

GUYON: Aaaaaaaaahhhhhhh!

BOATMAN: We're gonna die!

PALMER: (*Holds up his staff, the beasts all go away whimpering*) Everything's fine.

GUYON: (*Faking a laugh*) Heh heh . . . yeah . . . we knew it would be okay . . . we were just joking! Heh heh . . .

PALMER: (*Shaking his head again*) Come on!

(*They walk up to the entrance of the Bower and meet* GENIUS.)

GENIUS: Well hello, one and all! May I give you a bit of wine and tell you of your fortunes to come?

PALMER: Shut it! (*He knocks the wine over and hits* GENIUS *in the stomach with his staff.*) Maybe this'll toughen you up a bit!

(GUYON *and the* PALMER *continue on until they come across* EXCESS.)

EXCESS: Hello boys! Wouldn't you care for a sip of my sweet drink?

PALMER: We'll have none of it, you wicked wench! (*He knocks her wine to the ground, and* EXCESS *storms off angrily.*)

(*They continue until they come to the fountain where two maidens are bathing.* GUYON *begins to approach them when he is rebuked by the* PALMER.)

PALMER: GUYON! Get over here!

GUYON: Oh man . . . I'm sorry.

PALMER: We'll take care of those problems in a bit. But first we must face down Acrasia.

(*Finally they come to a clearing where* ACRASIA *has just put a young man under her spell.*)

PALMER: (*Whispering*) Ready? One . . . two . . . three . . . charge! (GUYON *and the* PALMER *charge in and throw a net over the two lovers.*)

GUYON: Ha-ha! Now we've got you!

PORTER: Now do as I say, Guyon. Do not pity any of these pleasant bowers! Go and tear them down! Uproot the beautiful gardens for they are filled with this witch's poison! Tear down every building and every house! This place shall no longer hold captives under its spells! You are the Knight of Temperance; destroy all that stands in your way!

(*A couple of days later* GUYON *and the* PALMER *are leaving. The beasts come rushing at them again.*)

GUYON: Oh great. Here they go again. Hey, Palmer! Do your thing!

PALMER: (*Raising his staff*) Watch this! (*Suddenly the beasts are turned back into men.*)

GRILL: (*Snorting*) Hey! You can't turn us back into men! That's no fair! Turn us back! Turn us back! We want to be beasts! We love the mud and the dirt and the yucky smells! Yucky! Yucky! Yucky! Turn us back!

(*The* PALMER *and* GUYON *look at each other, confused.*)

GUYON: (*Shrugging his shoulders and shaking his head*) Let Grill be Grill and have his hoggish mind. But as for us . . . let's go find pleasant winds and sail for more adventure!

THE END

CPSIA information can be obtained at www.ICGtesting.com
Printed in the USA
267442BV00002B/272/P

9 781591 280521